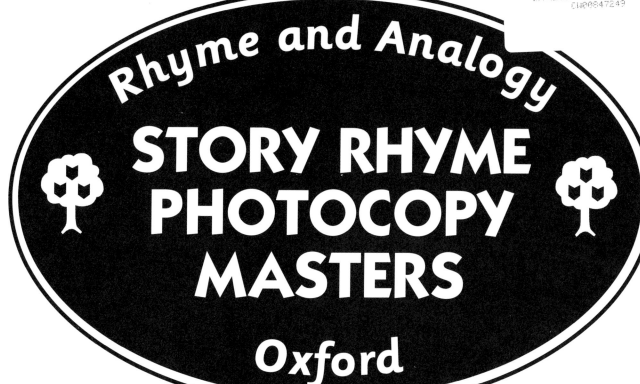

Rhyme and Analogy

STORY RHYME PHOTOCOPY MASTERS

Oxford

Clare Kirtley

Series Editor: Usha Goswami

Oxford University Press, Great Clarendon Street, Oxford, OX2 6DP

Oxford   New York
Athens   Auckland   Bangkok   Bogota   Bombay
Buenos Aires   Calcutta   Cape Town   Dar es Salaam   Delhi
Florence   Hong Kong   Istanbul   Karachi
Kuala Lumpur   Madras   Madrid   Melbourne
Mexico City   Nairobi   Paris   Singapore
Taipei   Tokyo   Toronto

and associated companies in
Berlin   Ibadan

Oxford is a trade mark of Oxford University Press

© Oxford University Press 1996

First published 1996

Reprinted 1996

ISBN 0 19 916805 9

Printed in Great Britain

Notes to accompany Story Rhyme Photocopy Masters

An awareness of the sound and letter patterns in language plays an important part in children's reading and spelling development. This awareness can be developed through an appreciation of rhyme. Young children often show a natural interest in rhyme, and find it easy to break words down into two parts: the initial sound before the vowel – the onset – and the rest of the word – the rime. For example, 'map' is divided into the onset 'm' and the rime 'ap'; 'trap' is made up of the onset 'tr' and the rime 'ap'.

By harnessing children's interest in rhymes, their attention can be focused on the sounds as well as the meaning of words, and on the common letter patterns that often represent these sounds. Children can use knowledge of rhyming letter patterns as a reading and spelling strategy when they meet new words. In this way, a child who knows the spelling pattern for 'king' – and understands that rhyming words often share spelling patterns – can, by analogy, use this knowledge to read and write rhyming words such as 'wing', 'ring', and 'sing'.

The sheets accompany twelve specially written Story Rhymes, which introduce rhyming family words in a genuine reading context. The Story Rhymes should be used alongside the activity sheets, beginning with aural rhyme work. Children should be encouraged to use the Story Rhymes, rhyme displays in class or previously completed sheets to check their work.

Using the sheets

These photocopiable sheets develop the child's ability to:
◆ listen to and appreciate rhymes
◆ recognize and read rhyming spelling patterns
◆ practise reading and writing rhymes.

There are listening (L), recognizing and reading (RR), and reading and writing (RW) activities for each Story Rhyme (see the grid on page 4, and the symbols on the sheets). A heading on each sheet indicates which Story Rhyme it is related to. Sheets relating to each Story Rhyme are grouped together, according to the type of activity, and in an order which reflects the level of difficulty. The teacher can choose the appropriate sheets to introduce, practise, reinforce, and assess knowledge of the rhyme families, according to the ability of each individual child. The sheets are presented in the advised reading order of the Story Rhymes. The family words increase in complexity throughout the Story Rhymes (from tub, wet, zip and fan in book 1 to grass, stung, kiss and cliff in book 12). Later sheets also reintroduce words encountered earlier. Sheets 115-124 at the end of this book are for general use and are not related to any one Story Rhyme. These sheets have been coded, but the level of difficulty may be adapted by the teacher (see below).

Simple instructions are included on each sheet for an adult to read with the child and so present the activity in a reading context. The instructions also provide a record of the activity for the child to share with others, for example, parents. A pencil symbol is used to demonstrate the activity to the child.

As a sheet is completed, the child should be encouraged to name any pictures and read the rhymes. The child will then be practising listening to rhymes and making the connection between the sounds of rhymes and the shared spelling patterns. Focus the child's attention on the common spelling patterns by asking him/her to use a coloured pen to highlight all the occurrences of the shared spelling pattern. Many of the sheets also contain rhyming words or verses. If the child is not yet ready to read these, they can be read by the teacher to draw the child's attention to the rhyming spelling pattern.

Opportunities for differentiation

Several of the sheets can be adapted, or extension activities used, to make them suitable for a wide range of ability levels. Many sheets have an optional section, indicated by a dotted cut line. As extension activities for many of the listening sheets, (see grid), the child could write the rhymes next to the pictures, or use the back of the sheet to create his/her own pictures of rhyming things, writing the matching rhyming words next to the pictures. An extension activity for the recognizing, reading and writing sheets, (see grid), is for the child to write simple sentences involving the rhyming words on the back of the sheet or in a separate sound book. Children should have been exposed to sufficient rhymes to offer their own suggestions when asked. The Story Rhymes should be used for ideas; nonsense words are acceptable if the child cannot think of a real word.

Pages 29 and 50 are designed to be folded in half and then in half again, creating a little rhyme book for the child to read.

Page 71 shows the child how to make a rhyming flip book. This activity can be extended and rhyme flip books made for lots of rhyme families. Other ways to make rhyming words can also be investigated such as word wheels and letter dice (see *Teacher's Guide*).

A number of the sheets require the child to complete sentences or rhyming families by writing rhymes. On page 60, children can provide *any* rhymes, or the teacher could direct them by writing in the first word. In most cases, the rhymes are provided for the child in boxes at the bottom of the page (see pages 10, 18, 20, 38, 40, 48, 59, 68, 77, 85, 95, 102 and 110). The teacher can cover these boxes up before photocopying or cut the boxes off, so that the more able child has to come up with the rhymes him/herself.

Alternatively, the teacher can instruct the child to cut off the boxes along the dotted line and stick them to the back of the sheet. This makes the task harder for the child: the rhyming words are provided, but the child has to remember the spelling pattern when filling in the front of the sheet. Similarly the rhymes that are hidden in the grids are provided for the child in boxes at the bottom of the page and may be removed (see pages 26, 46, 74, 90 and 107).

General sheets

These general sheets provide further opportunities for practice or assessment, and

could be used to encourage the child to practise his/her rhyming knowledge with an adult at home.

Pages 118 to 120 are left blank for the teacher (or a more able child) to fill in. They can support any rhyming family, including those not introduced in the Story Rhymes. Page 119 gives practise in reading families of rhyming words; the common spelling pattern is emphasized by the teacher writing the differing onset of each word on a pen lid and the common rime on the corresponding pen body.

Pages 121 and 122 can be simplified and used as non-writing activity sheets if the instructions at the bottom are removed.

Pages 123 and 124 are designed to develop the child's comprehension skills. The blank spaces can be used by the child to draw or write the main elements from any one of the Story Rhymes. Alternatively the blank space on page 123 can be used to develop rhyme awareness by instructing the child to write or draw pictures of the rhyming words that occur in the story. As this blank space represents the back of the story book, the child could also create an advert in pictures or writing to encourage others to read the book, perhaps emphasizing the parts of the story the child liked best. The child can also be asked to create an interesting illustration from the story, in the space on the front of the book outline.

Note: The child should be introduced to the concept of rhyme through oral activities before using these sheets.

The sheets should be used with:

  Rhyme and Analogy Story Rhymes
  Pack A (0 19 916817 2) and
  Pack B (0 19 916825 3)
  Teacher's Guide (0 19 916833 4)

Also available are:

  Story Rhymes Tapes (0 19 916808 3)

For work on letter sounds, the following Rhyme and Analogy resources are available:

  Alphabet Photocopy Masters (0 19 916834 2)
  Card Games (0 19 916791 5)
  Alphabet frieze (0 19 916789 3)
  Tabletop Alphabet Pack (01 916790 7)

These sheets support twelve Story Rhymes. Each Story Rhyme introduces four rhyming word families, represented by a clue word from the family.

For each Story Rhyme there are three types of sheet. An explanation of the three types of sheet is given in the introductory notes to this book.

Title	Word families	Listening activities (by page) **L**	Recognizing and reading activities (by page) **RR**	Reading and writing activities (by page) **RW**
Supersonic engine juice	tub net zip fan	1–6	7–8	9–10
Scat, cat!	cat pin bed dog	11–15	16–17	18–20
The Mungle Flap	cap hen nut lid	21–22	23–26	27–30
Bad day, good day	sad hit leg sun	31–33	34–35	36–40
Who wants to play with a troll?	wig jam shop hay	41–42	43–46	47–50
The Spell Shell	swim crab knot bell	51–53	54–56	57–60
That's nothing	bag hill mum duck	61	62–64	65–69
Rockpool rap	knob ball snow star	70	71–75	76–78
The King's socks	clock king plug flash	79–80	81–82	83–87
Gran, Gran!	sack long brush dress	88	89–90	91–96
How to kick-start a dragon	puff cross bang chick	97	98–100	101–105
My home	grass stung kiss cliff	106	107	108–114
General	practice of above rhymes	117	115–116	
	any rhyme family		118–120	121–124

Name

Colour the things in the picture which rhyme with fan .

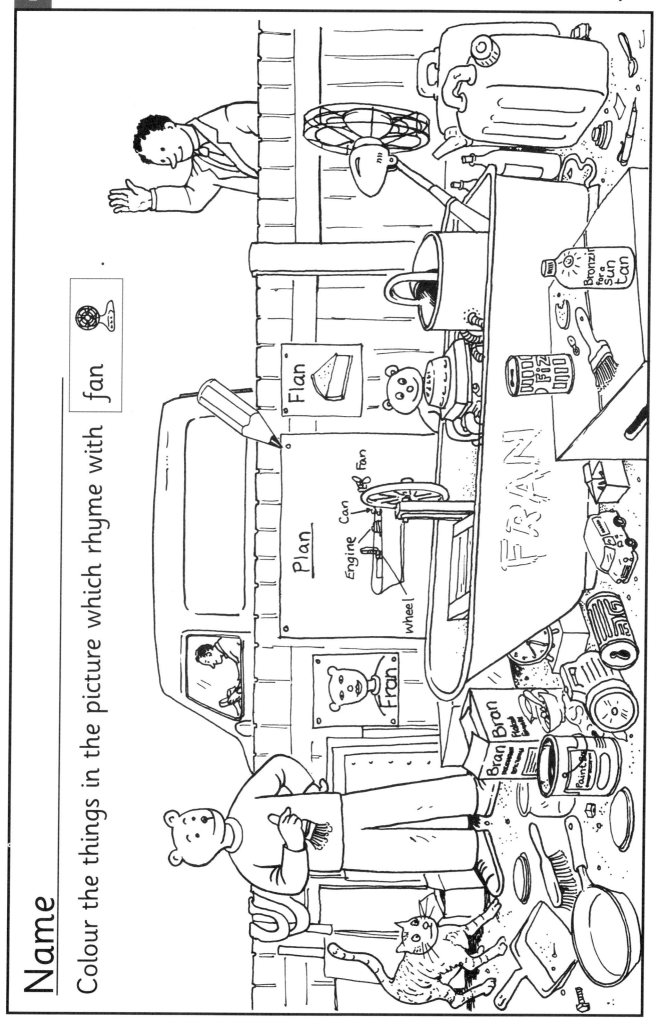

Name

Join up the rhymes.

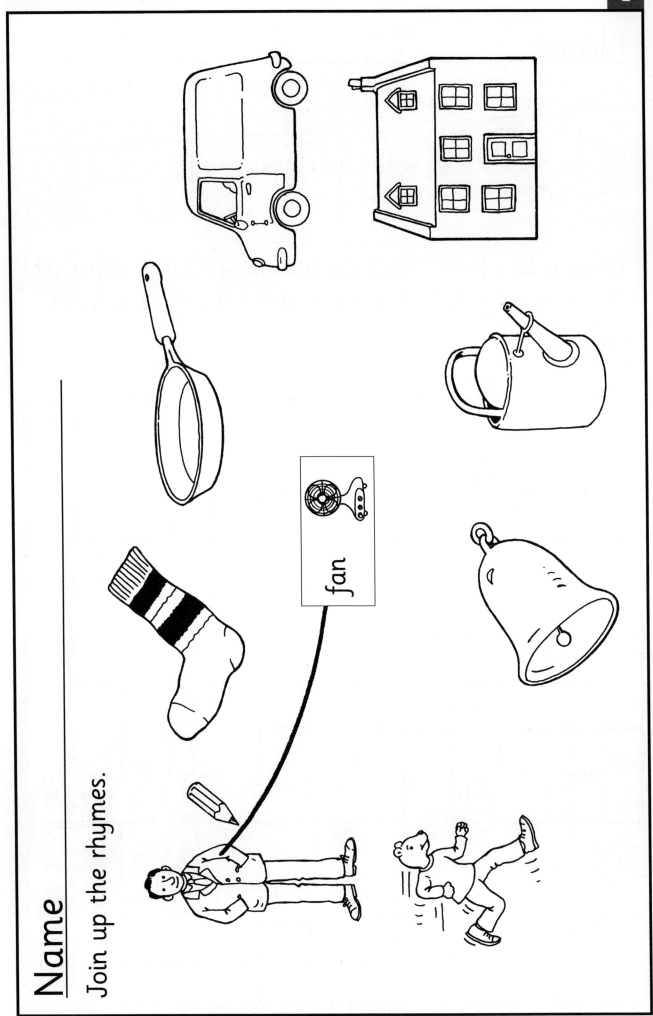

fan

Name

McGinty turned to Alex and he said, 'I bet –
that old tin tub will never catch my super jet!'

Draw a line from Alex's tin tub to McGinty's super jet. You can only go through pictures which rhyme with

zip

.

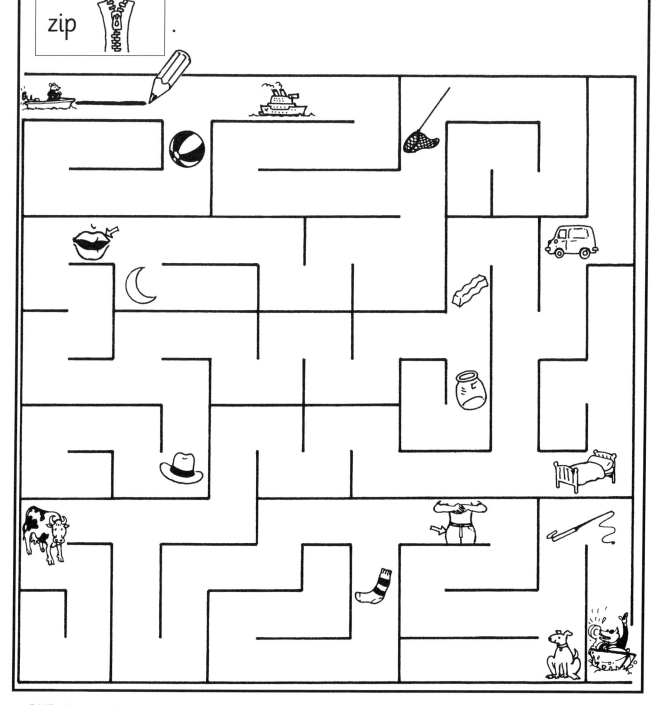

Name

Get the pet
to the vet
but don't get wet!

Colour the stepping stones which rhyme

with pet .

Name

Find the boat which rhymes.

Name

Join up the anchor which rhymes with each boat.

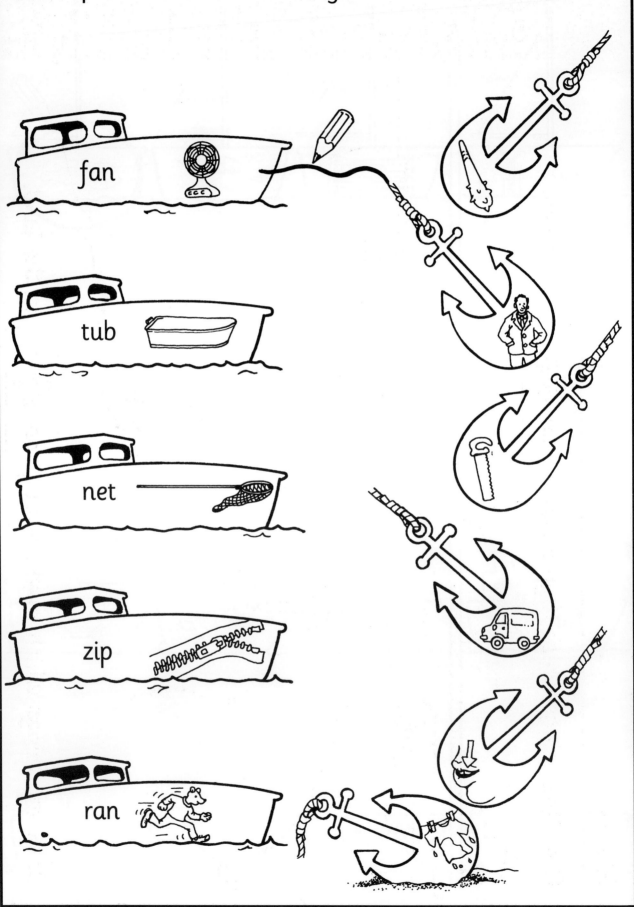

fan

tub

net

zip

ran

man

chip

fan

lip

whip

plan

zip

can

pan

Name

Draw the things which rhyme with | ship | on the sea.

Draw the things which rhyme with | van | on the land.

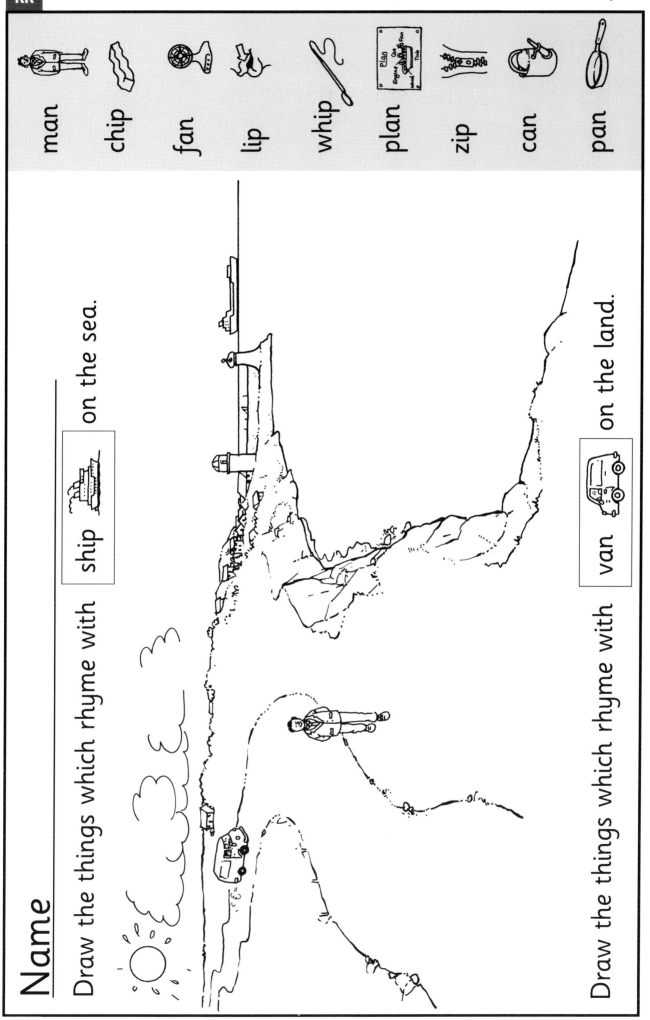

Name

Colour the pictures which rhyme in each bubble.

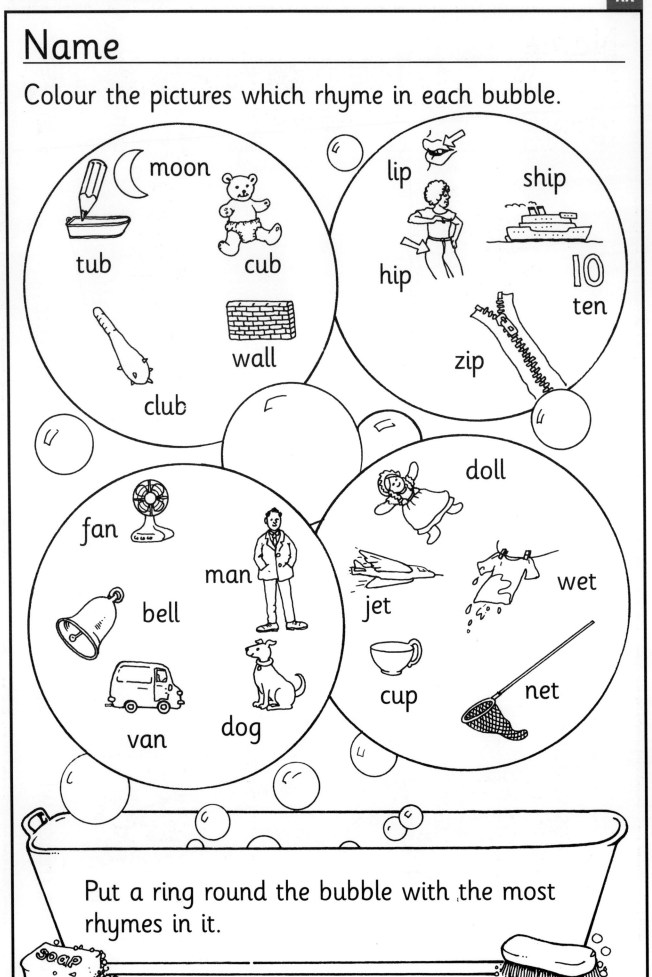

moon
tub   cub
wall
club

lip   ship
hip   ten
zip

fan
man
bell
van   dog

doll
jet   wet
cup   net

Put a ring round the bubble with the most rhymes in it.

Name _____

Use the end of $\boxed{f}$ $\boxed{a\ n}$ to finish these rhymes.

$\boxed{r}$ $\boxed{a\ n}$

$\boxed{m}$ $\boxed{}$

$\boxed{c}$ $\boxed{}$

$\boxed{p}$ $\boxed{}$

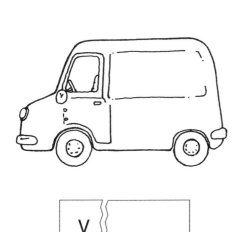

$\boxed{v}$ $\boxed{}$

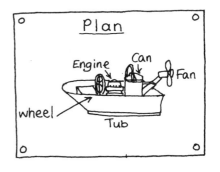

$\boxed{pl}$ $\boxed{}$

Name

Write the rhymes in the boxes.

Alex can see a whip
in the | **ship** | .

Alex can see a cub
in the | | .

Alex can see a jet
in the | | .

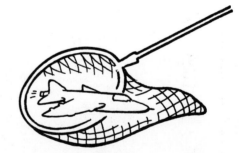

Alex can see a man
in the | | .

| van 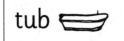 | ship | tub | net |

L

Name

Colour the things in the picture which rhyme with | cat |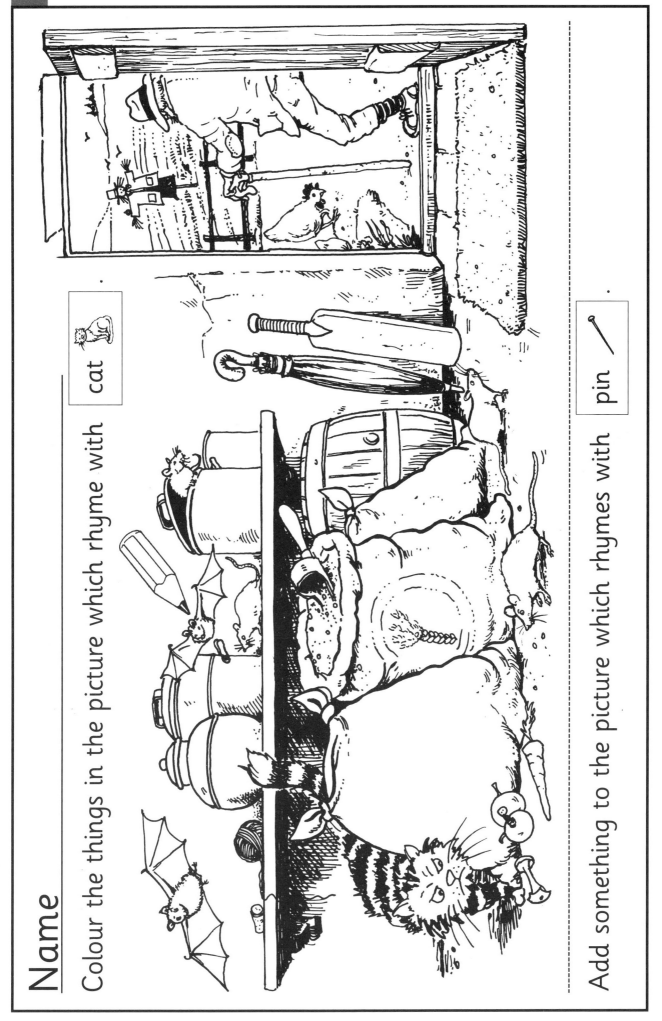

Add something to the picture which rhymes with | pin |

Name

Colour the parts of the mouse which have pictures

rhyming with | pin ✐ | on them.

Write the word that the coloured parts make.

Name

Join up the rhymes.

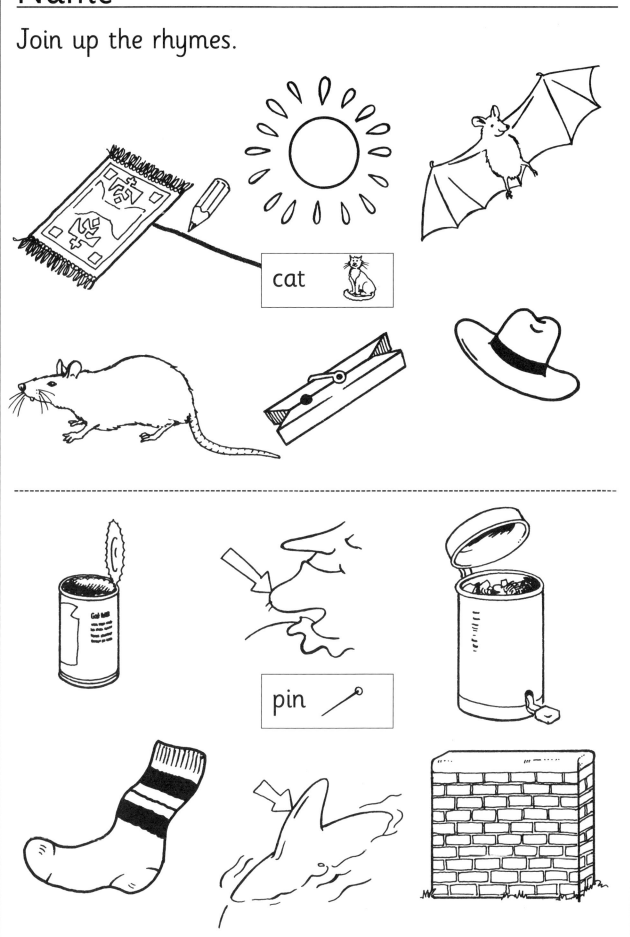

cat

pin

Name

Find the rhymes.

mat

dog

chin

rat

Name

Join up the mat which rhymes with each cat.

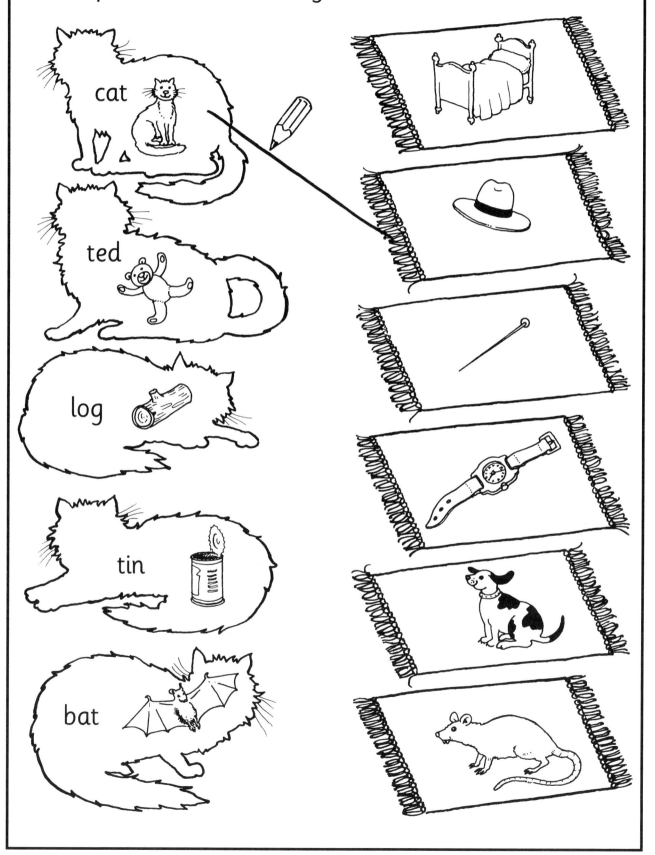

Name

Colour the pictures which rhyme in each cup.

dog

bun

log

cog

pin

tin

fin

leg

bed

shed

van

ted

cat

bat

peg

mat

rat

Draw rhyming pictures in this cup.

Name

The pictures in each sack rhyme.
Put rings round the right words.

(bed) bat

shop shed

ted tap

cup cat

mat mop

bun bat

hat hum

run rat

peg pin

tin tub

chin chop

bus bin

fed fin

dog dim

lid log

cup cog

frog frill

Put a ring round the sack with the fewest
rhymes in it.

RW

Name

Write rhymes on the pictures.

dog
cog

cat

bed

frog

rat

shed

log

mat

hat

ted

cog

RW

Name

Use the end of | c | a t | to finish these rhymes.

| m | at |

| b | |

| r | |

| h | |

| s | |

| p | |

19

Name

Write the rhymes in the empty boxes.

Asleep in her basket,

was Mrs Moore's cat ,

while her dog was curled up

on his favourite .

Old Mrs Moore

was asleep in her bed .

Her nightcap was white,

and her nightdress was .

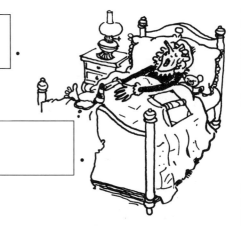

Now, there in the fireplace

still burned a small log .

And it spat out a spark,

on the nose of the .

| dog | mat | red |

Name

Colour the things in the picture which rhyme with | cap | .

Add something to the picture which rhymes with | hen |

Name

Join up the rhymes.

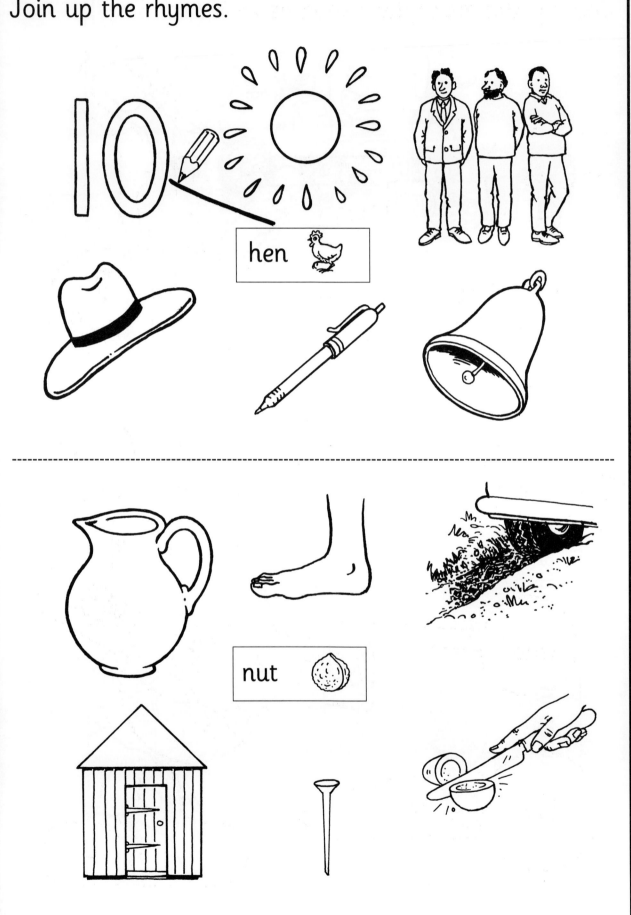

hen

nut

Name

Join up the lock which rhymes with each key.

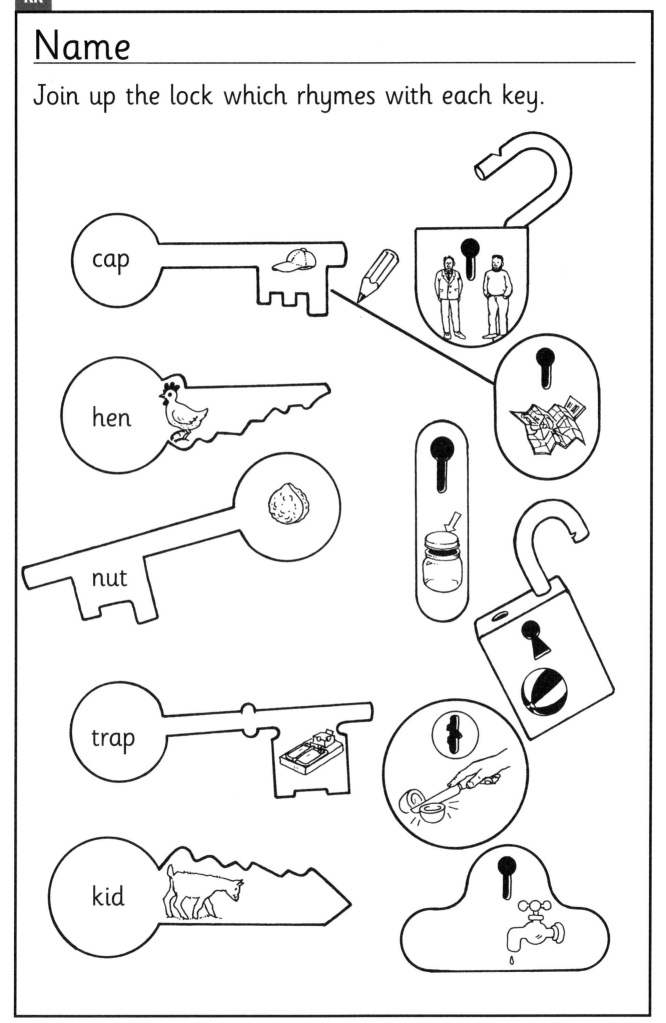

Name

Here is a map.

Colour the nut 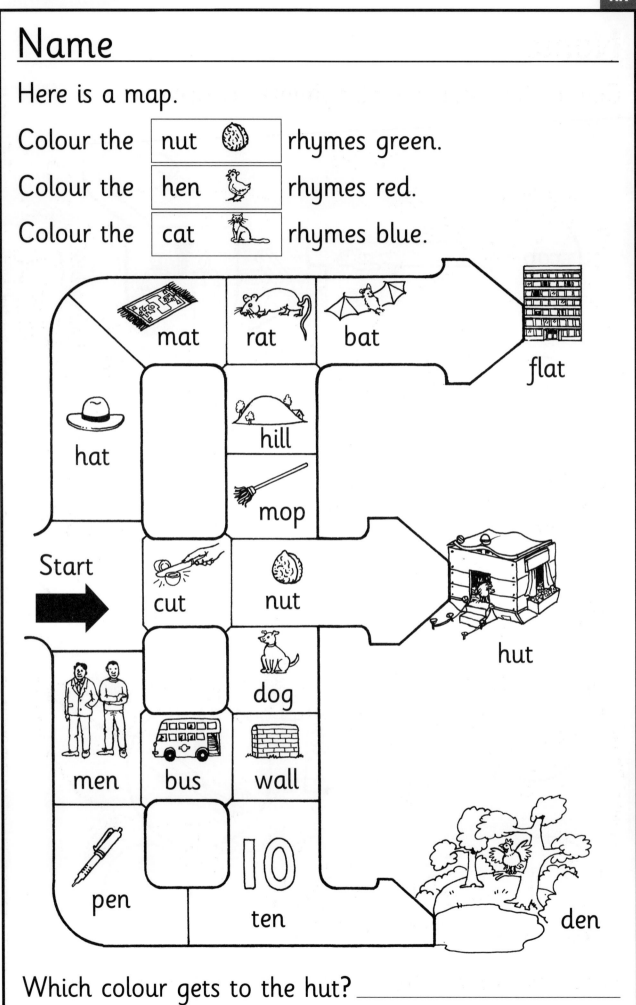 rhymes green.

Colour the hen rhymes red.

Colour the cat rhymes blue.

mat

rat

bat

flat

hat

hill

mop

Start

cut

nut

hut

dog

men

bus

wall

pen

10

ten

den

Which colour gets to the hut? _____

Name

Colour the pictures which rhyme in each Mungle Flap.

Put a ring round the one with the most rhymes in it.

Name

Here is a grid. Put a ring round all the words which rhyme with grid ⊞ .

o	d	i	d	s	t
r	s	q	u	i	d
k	i	d	x	a	v
m	b	h	i	d	f
s	k	i	d	n	y
c	g	h	l	i	d

kid	lid	skid
hid	squid 	

Name

Write these letters in the drips to make rhymes.

t	c	l	m	n

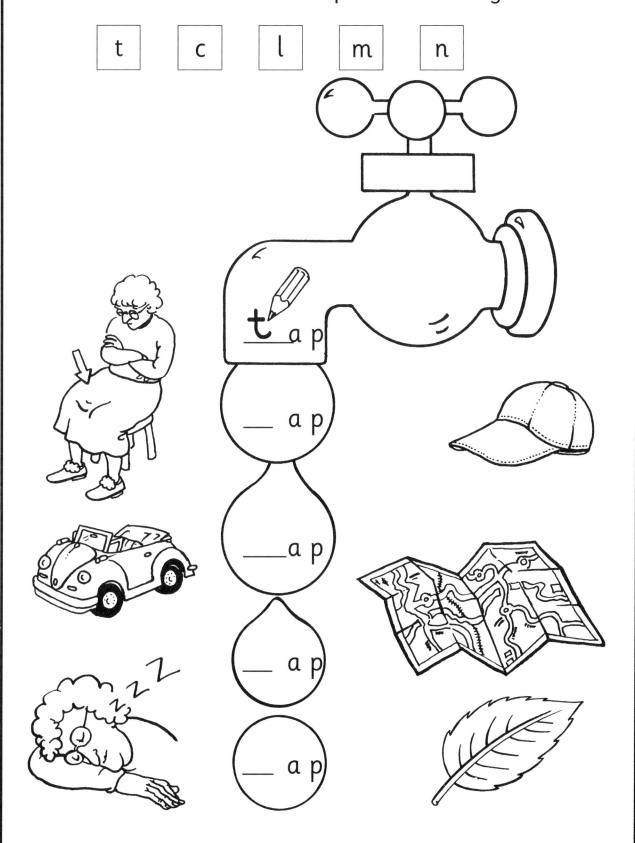

t __ a p

___ a p

___ a p

___ a p

___ a p

Draw lines from the words to the pictures.

Name

Use the end of c | a p   or the end of

l | i d  to finish these rhymes.

l | **ap**

k |

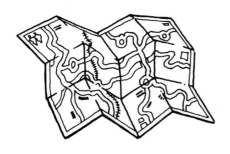

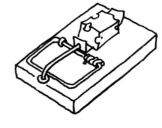

m |

tr |

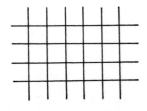

gr |

n |

t |

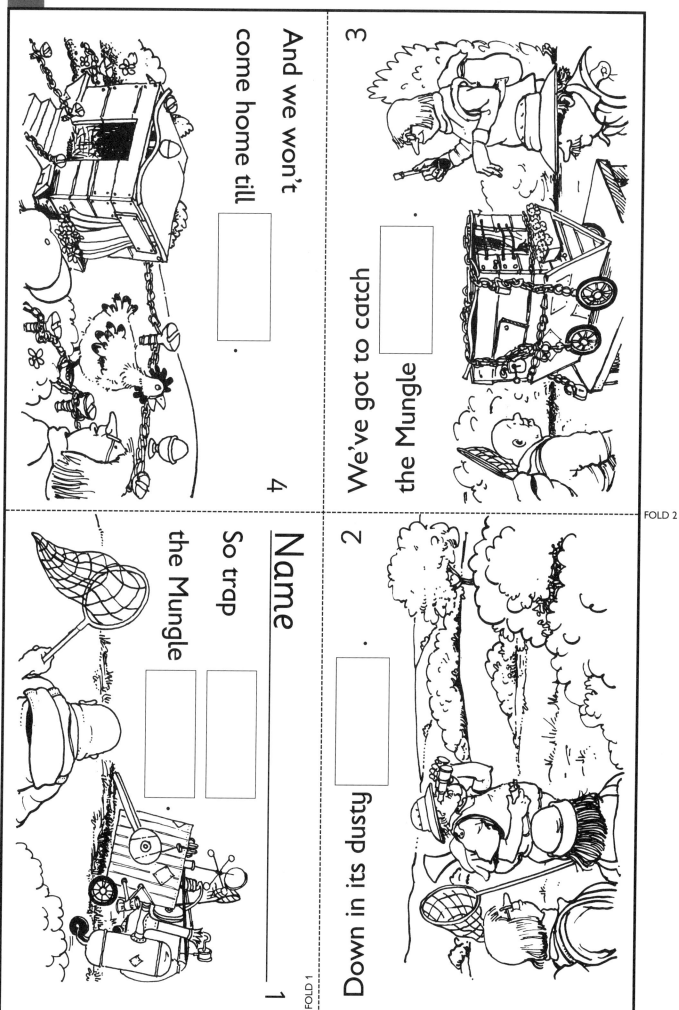

And we won't
come home till

4

We've got to catch
the Mungle

3

Name

So trap
the Mungle

1

FOLD 1

Down in its dusty

2

FOLD 2

29

Name

Colour the eggs which rhyme in each basket.

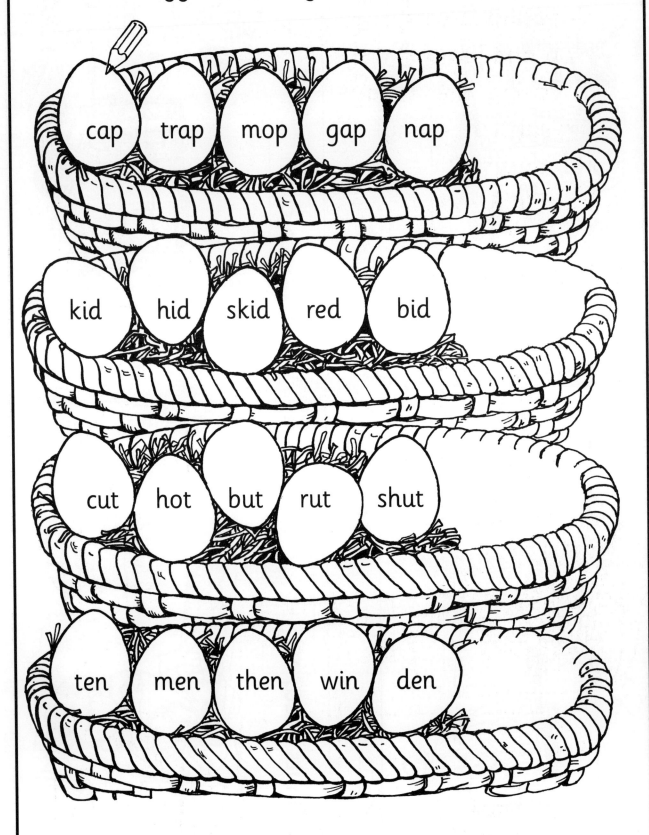

cap trap mop gap nap

kid hid skid red bid

cut hot but rut shut

ten men then win den

Add an egg which rhymes to each basket.

Name

But Sunday was a fun day.
Hop and jump and run – day.
A closing eyes – day.
Big surprise – day.
Fun and mirth – day...
It's my birthday!

Colour the pictures which rhyme with sun.

Name

Join up the knitting which rhymes with the balls of wool.

Name

Find the shirt which rhymes.

Name

Colour the pictures which rhyme in each ball of wool.

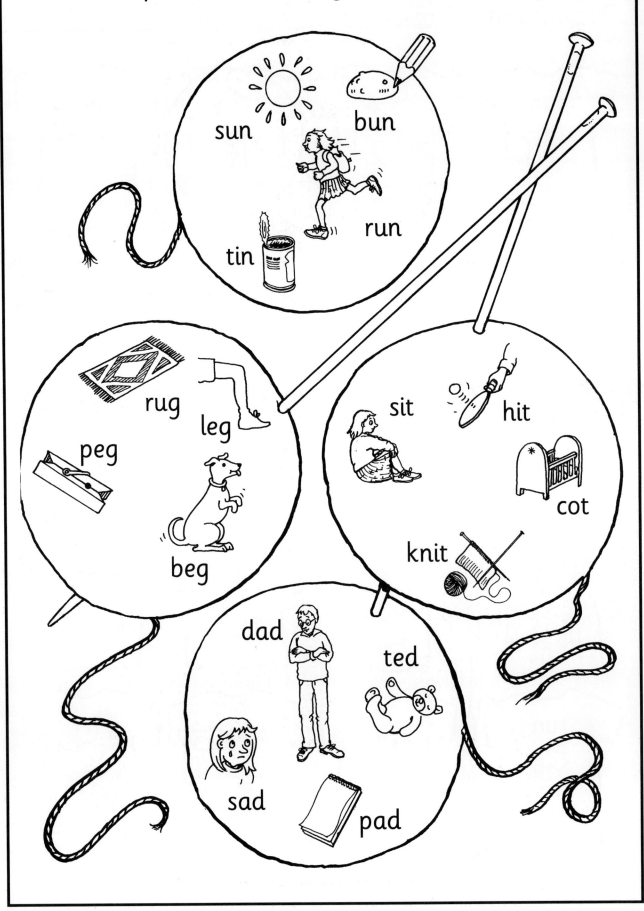

Name

The pictures in each bun rhyme.
Put rings round the right words.

lip	(leg)
peg	pot
beg	bus

hit	hop
sad	sit
knit	knock
pit	pan

sun	sock
red	run
bun	bat

Draw rhyming pictures in this bun.

Name

Write these letters on the sun to make rhymes.

| s | b | f | n | r |

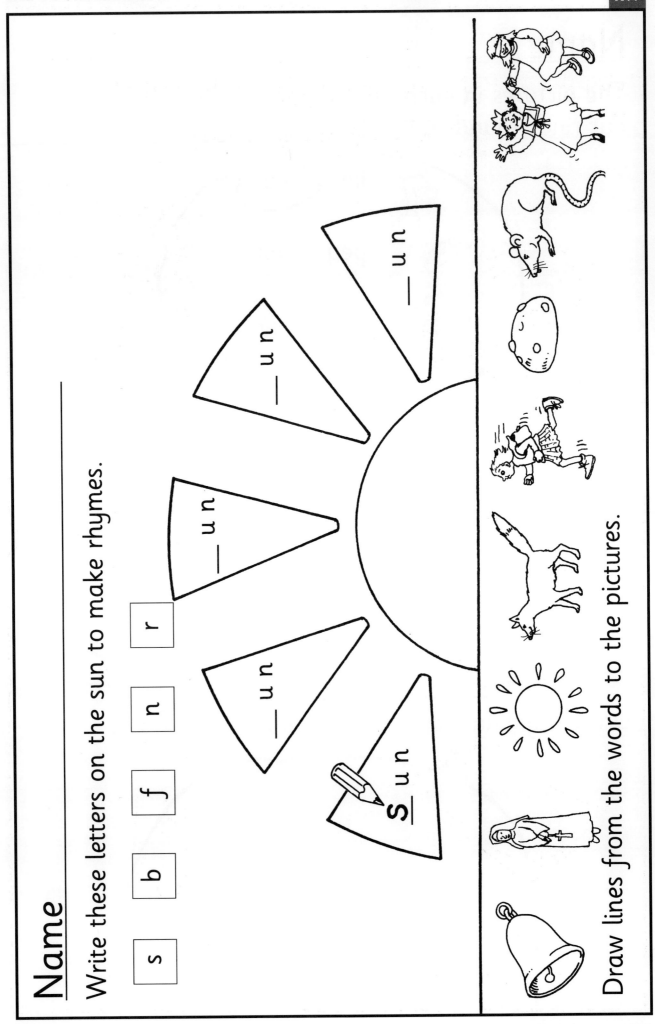

_ u n

_ u n

_ u n

_ u n

s u n

Draw lines from the words to the pictures.

Name

Use the end of │ s │ u n │ or the end of

│ s │ a d │  to finish these rhymes.

│ m │ **a d** │

│ r │ │

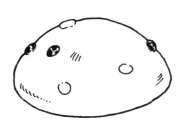

│ b │ │

│ D │ │

│ p │ │

│ n │ │

Name

Write the rhymes in the boxes and finish the pictures.

I like to have a bun
which is ☐ fun .

I like to sit
and ☐ .

I like to make Dad
go ☐ .

I like to beg
on one ☐ .

But most of all
I like to run
in the ☐ .

sun 	fun 	knit 	leg	mad 

Name

Colour the cakes which rhyme on each plate.

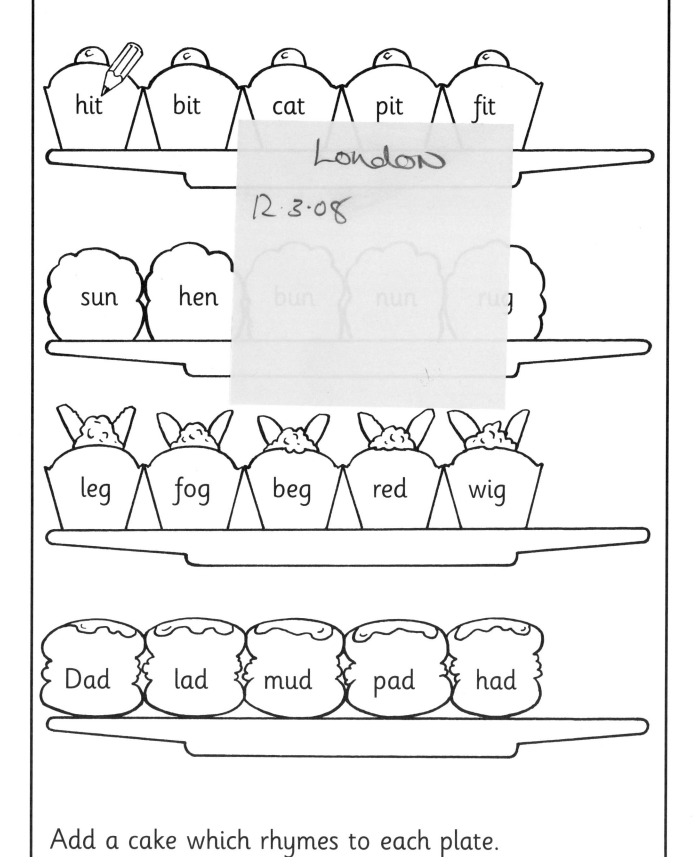

London
12.3.08

hit   bit   cat   pit   fit

sun   hen   bun   nun   rug

leg   fog   beg   red   wig

Dad   lad   mud   pad   had

Add a cake which rhymes to each plate.

Name

Write rhymes on the lunch boxes.

sad

Dad

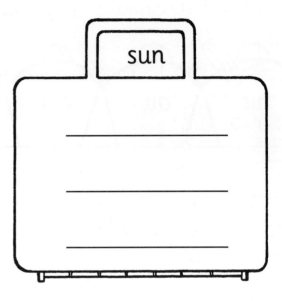

sun

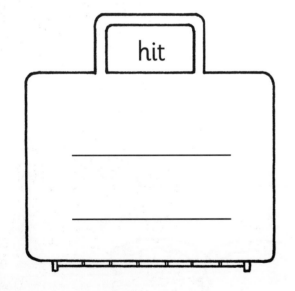

hit

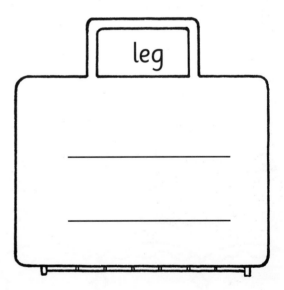

leg

kit	beg	Dad	bun
bad	run	bit	peg	fun

Name

'I must pop to the shop, and buy
some dragons' eggs for tea.'

Colour the things in the picture which rhyme with

shop .

Add something to the shop which rhymes with

jam .

Name

Find the egg which rhymes.

shop

twig

pram

tray

chop

Name

'Children never play with trolls,
at least not every day.
But if I find my way to them,
they may just want to play.'

Draw a line from Little Troll to the children.
You can only go through pictures and words which

rhyme with | tray 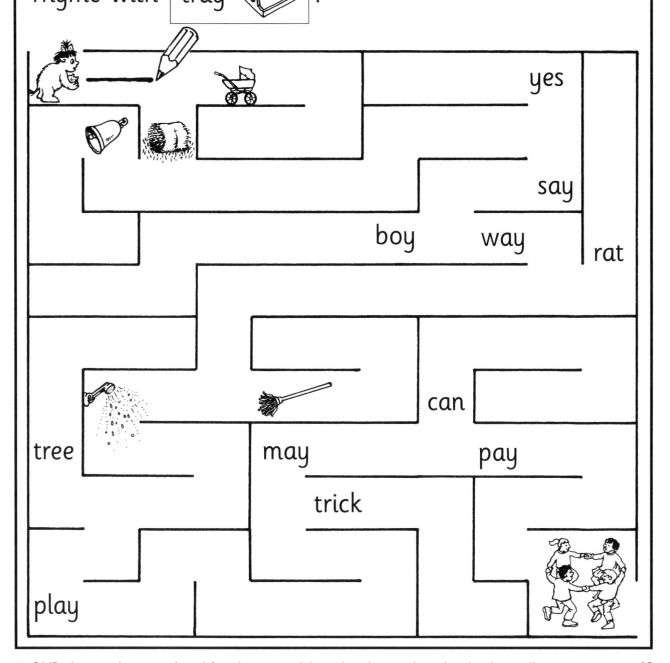 .

Name

The pictures in each jam rhyme.
Put rings round the right words.

(jam) jet

ram red

hut ham

dog day

tray tree

hay hen

pan pig

dig den

wet wig

shop shell

man mop

tin top

chop chat

Put a ring round the jam with the most rhymes in it.

Name

Put rings round the right words.

May we play with the | top / hop | ?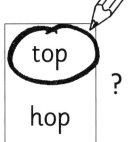

May we play with the | wig / big | ?

May we play with the | yam / jam | ?

May we play with the | pop / mop | ?

May we play with the | tray / pray | ?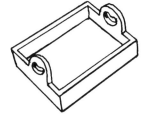

Name

Put a ring round all the words which rhyme with

wig .

k	h	c	(w	i	g)
n	d	i	g	w	s
t	w	i	g	a	i
b	m	f	i	g	l
b	i	g	p	r	f
s	i	j	i	g	d

---

twig	jig	big
fig	dig	

Name

Use the end of | j | a m |  to finish these rhymes.

Draw lines from the words to the pictures.

Name

Write rhymes in the shop windows.

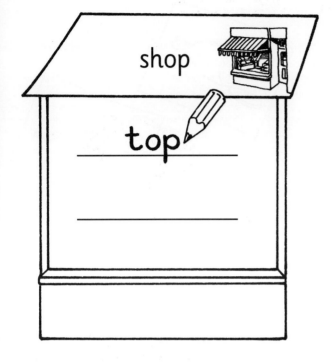

shop

top

_____

_____

wig

_____

_____

hay

_____

_____

jam

_____

_____

tray  ham  twig mop

dig  top  dam spray

Name

Use the end of | j | a m | or the end of
| h | a y | to finish these rhymes.

| r | am |

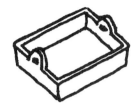

| tr | |

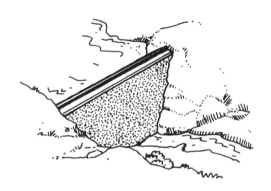

| d | |

| pr | |

| d | |

| h | |

FOLD 1

RW

3

I've eaten so much
party food,

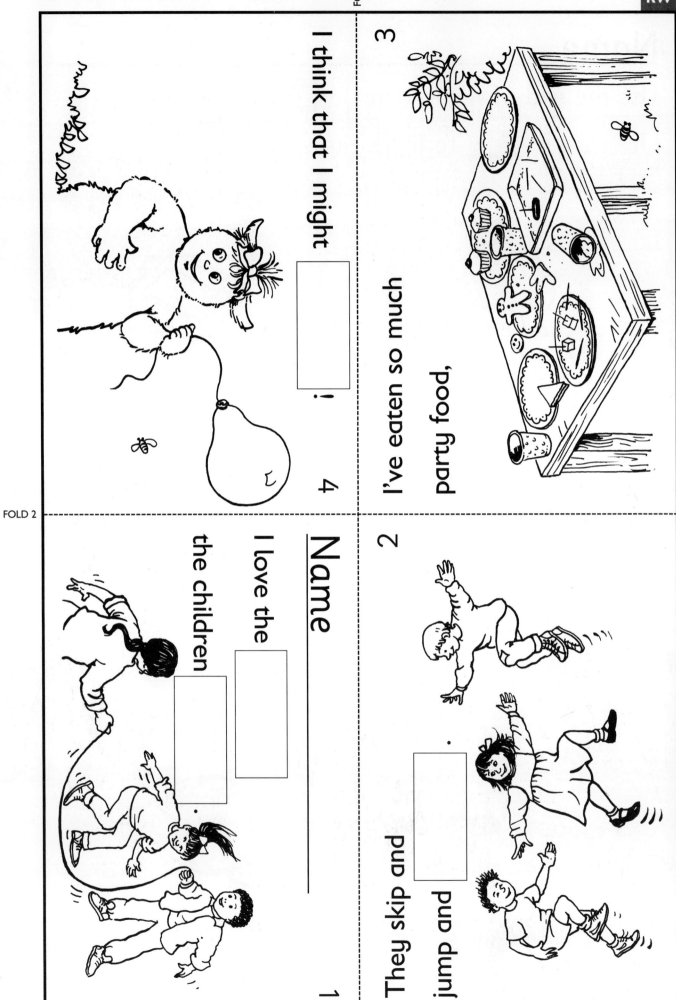

I think that I might

□ !

4

2

They skip and
jump and

□

Name ____

I love the

□

the children

□

1

FOLD 2

Name

'All creatures who live
in the salty blue swell
will come to my side
when I blow on this shell.'

Colour the things in the picture which rhyme with

shell .

Add something to the picture which rhymes

with | knot 🪢 | .

Name

Colour the parts of the shell which have pictures

rhyming with | fell  | on them.

Write the word that the coloured parts make.

Name

Find the shell which rhymes.

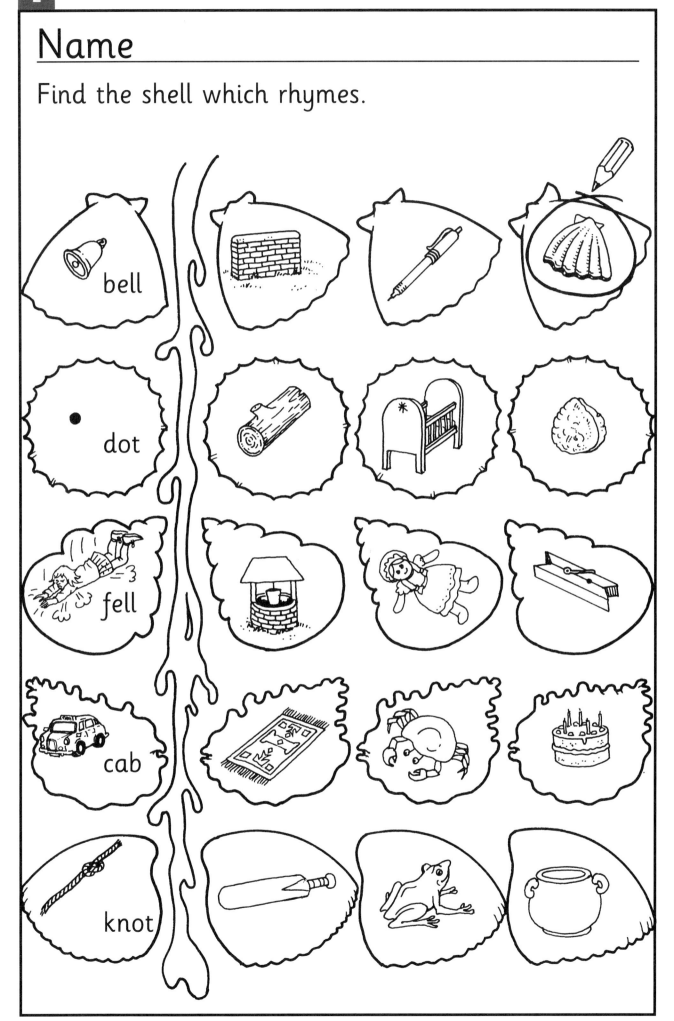

bell

dot

fell

cab

knot

Name

These strange horses trot
gently over the sand.
They come to the spot
where the two children stand.

Draw a line from the horses to the children.
You can only go through pictures and words which
rhyme with | cot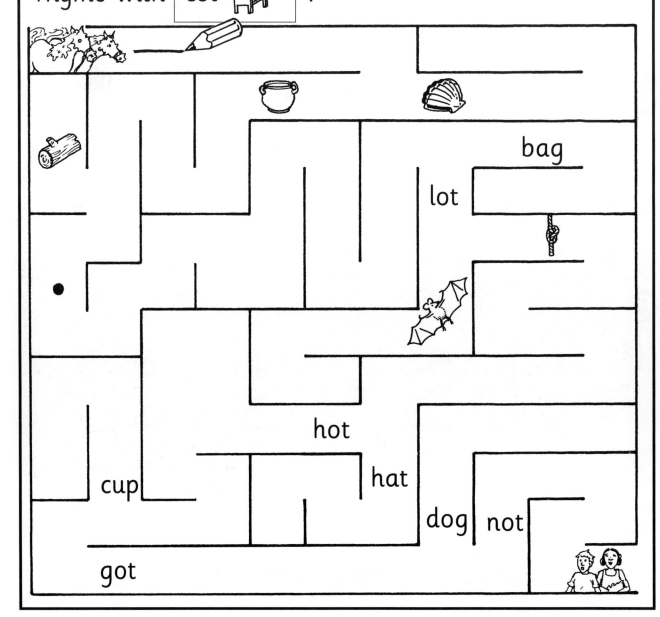

bag

lot

hot

cup

hat

dog | not

got

Name _____

Swim to King Neptune.

Colour the crabs which rhyme with | swim  | red.
Colour the crabs which rhyme with | crab | blue.
Colour the crabs which rhyme with | shell | green.

fell

him

bell

well

dim

cab

yell

tell

sell

rim

grab

Which colour gets to King Neptune?_____

Name _____

The children are thinking of things which rhyme with their names.
Draw or write some rhymes.

Can you think of something which rhymes with someone's name?
Draw or write it here.

Name _____

Name

Write these letters on the robot to make rhymes.

| p | c | d | h | kn |

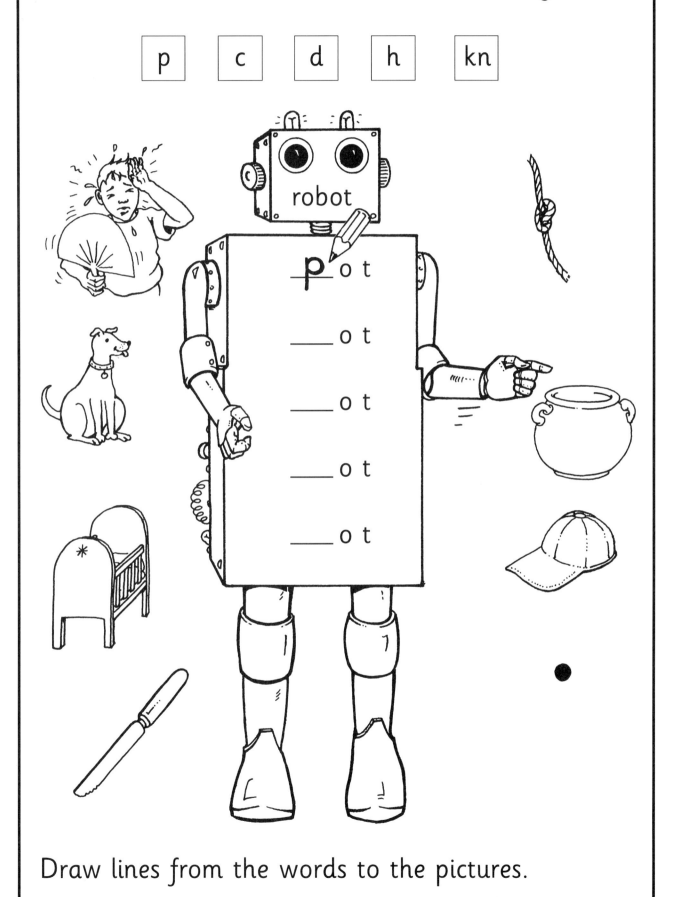

p o t

___ o t

___ o t

___ o t

___ o t

Draw lines from the words to the pictures.

Name

Use the end of | b { e l l | 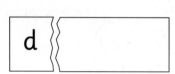 or the end of

| kn { o t | to finish these rhymes.

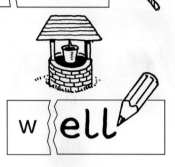

| w { ell |    • | d { |

| c { | | sh { |

| f { | | p { |

Write the rhyming words in the bells.

bell

knot

Name _____

Finish the rhyming sentences.

Down by the sea,
where the waves slip and skim,
two children are playing
while the sea creatures _____ .

Their manes shine with bubbles
that hang dot by dot.
Their harness is tied
in a silvery _____ .

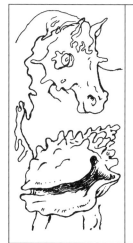

Then one of them speaks –
'You have done very well.
We've been searching the seas
for King Neptune's lost _____ .'

| knot | shell | swim |

Name

'Welcome,' says Neptune
(the King of the Sea).
'I'm delighted you've brought back
the Spell Shell to me.'

Write a family of rhyming words on each shell.

shell
fell

Name

Find the truck which rhymes.

Name

'How's this for a thrill?
My Mum can ski downhill.
I call that skill.'

Draw a line from Mum to the bottom of the hill.
You can only go through pictures and words which

rhyme with hill .

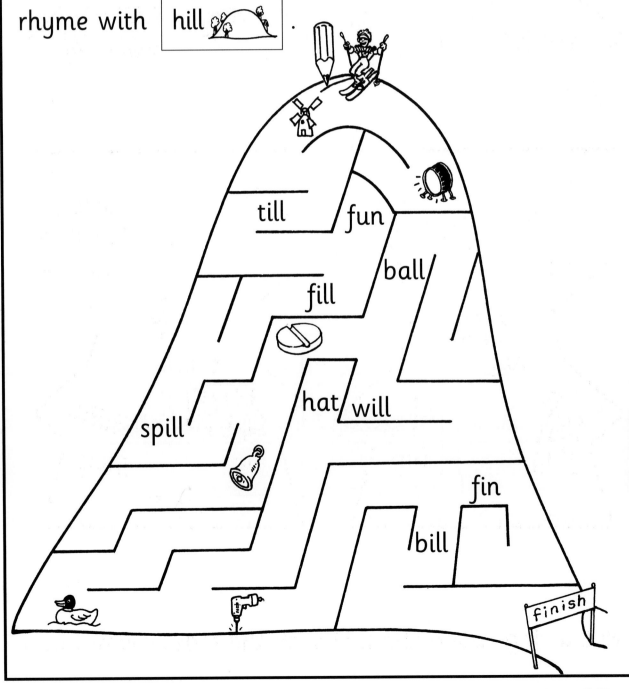

till   fun
ball
fill
hat will
spill
fin
bill
finish

Name

Colour the pictures which rhyme in each mill.

Put a ring round the mill with the most rhymes in it.

Name

The pictures in each drum rhyme.
Put rings round the right words.

drop (drum)

Mum   mat

plum   plot

bag   bin

flop   flag

rag   ran

hill   had

man   mill

dress   drill

pill   peg

doll   duck

sat   suck

truck   trap

Draw rhyming pictures in this drum.

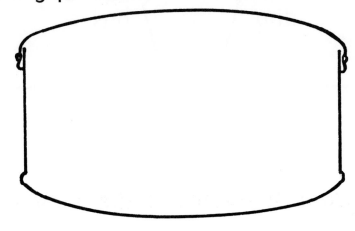

Name

Write these letters on the bag to make rhymes.

b	fl	r	t	w

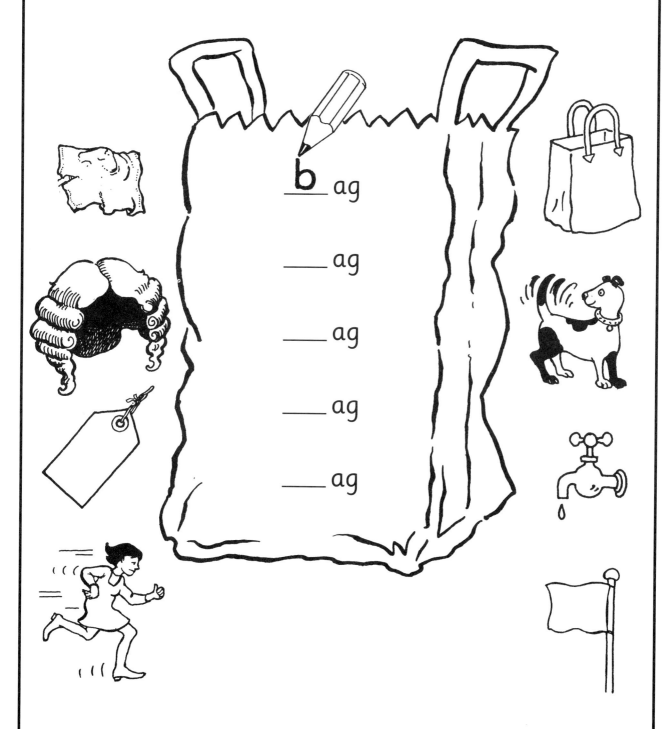

b_ ag

___ ag

___ ag

___ ag

___ ag

Draw lines from the words to the pictures.

Name

Colour the flags which rhyme on each pole.

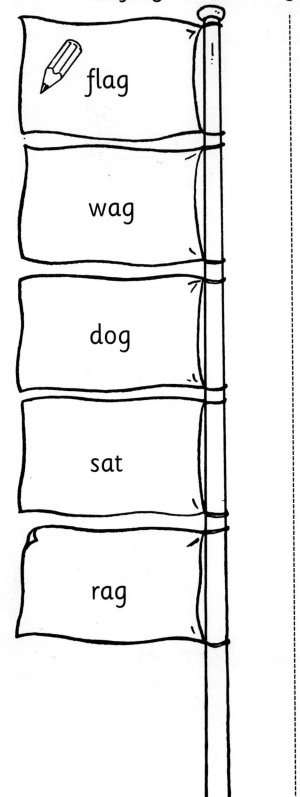
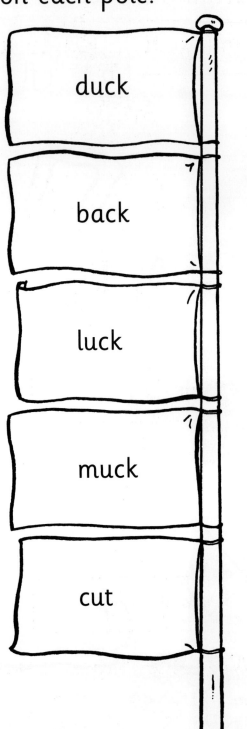

Add a rhyming flag to each pole.

Name

Use the end of h { ill   or the end of

m { u m   to finish these rhymes.

t { i l l

m {

dr {

p {

$4 + 3 = 7$

s {

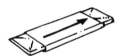

g {

Write the rhyming words on the pictures.

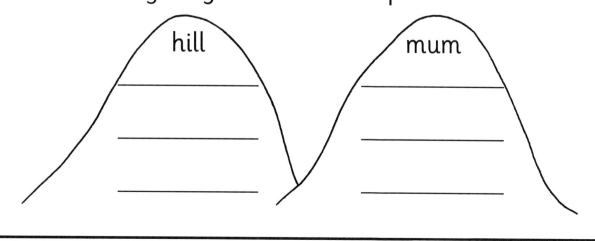

hill   mum

Name _____

Finish the rhyming sentences.

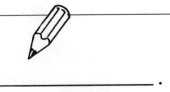

My Mum can put up a flag,
and parachute down in a paper _____.

My Mum saw a truck
stuck in some _____.

My Mum can play a drum
blow a trumpet and _____.

| muck | hum | bag |

Name

Colour the words which rhyme on the front wheel.
Turn the page to read each word.

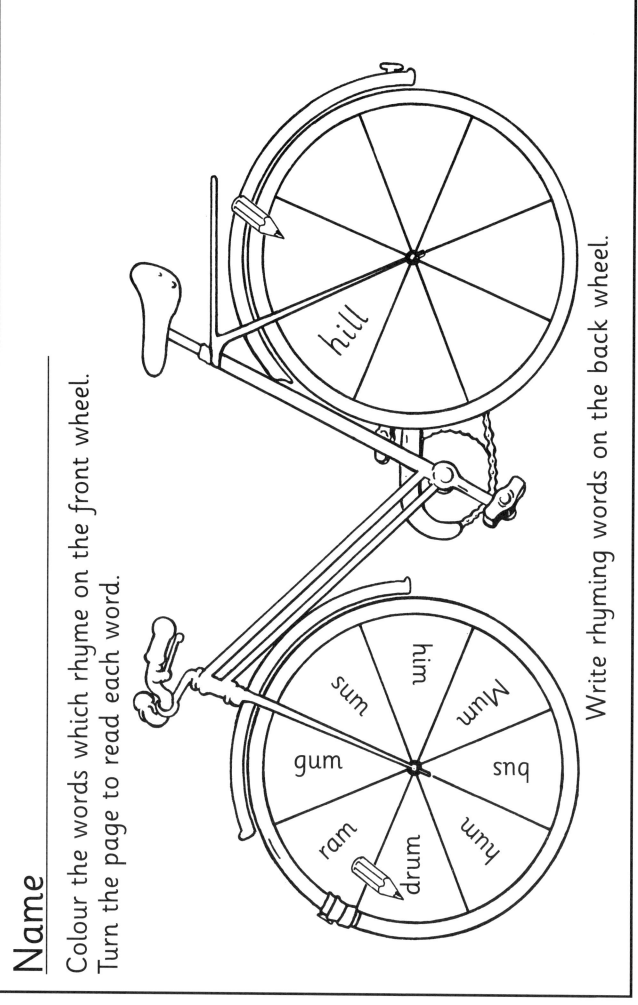

hill

sum

him

gum

Mum

ram

bus

drum

hum

Write rhyming words on the back wheel.

Name

Join up the guitars which rhyme.

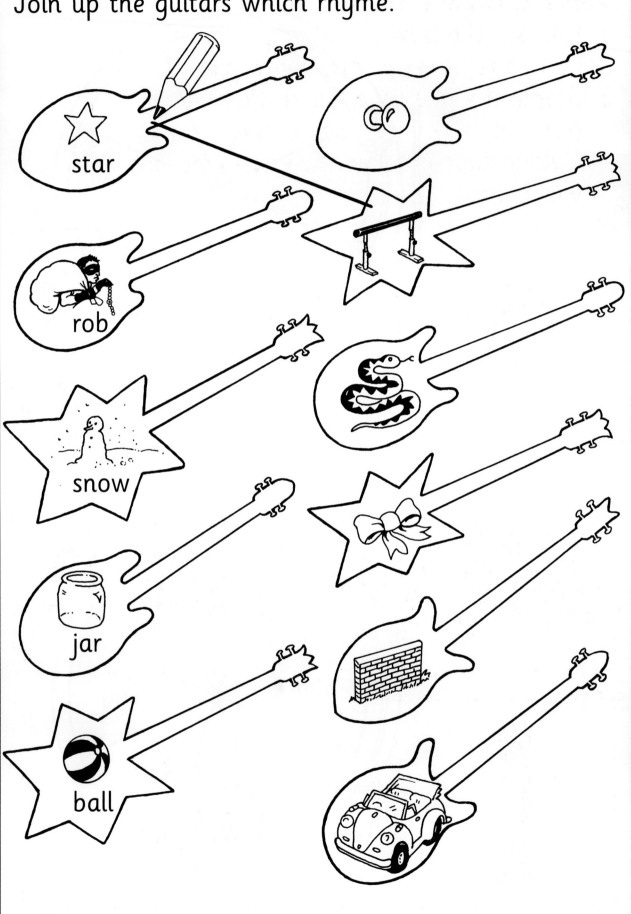

Name

Make a rhyme book

1 Cut out the boxes.
2 Place the boxes in order in a pile.
3 Staple the pile together so that the pictures are above each other.
4 Colour each picture when you can read each word.

Name

Colour the parts of the shark which have

pictures or words rhyming with | ball | 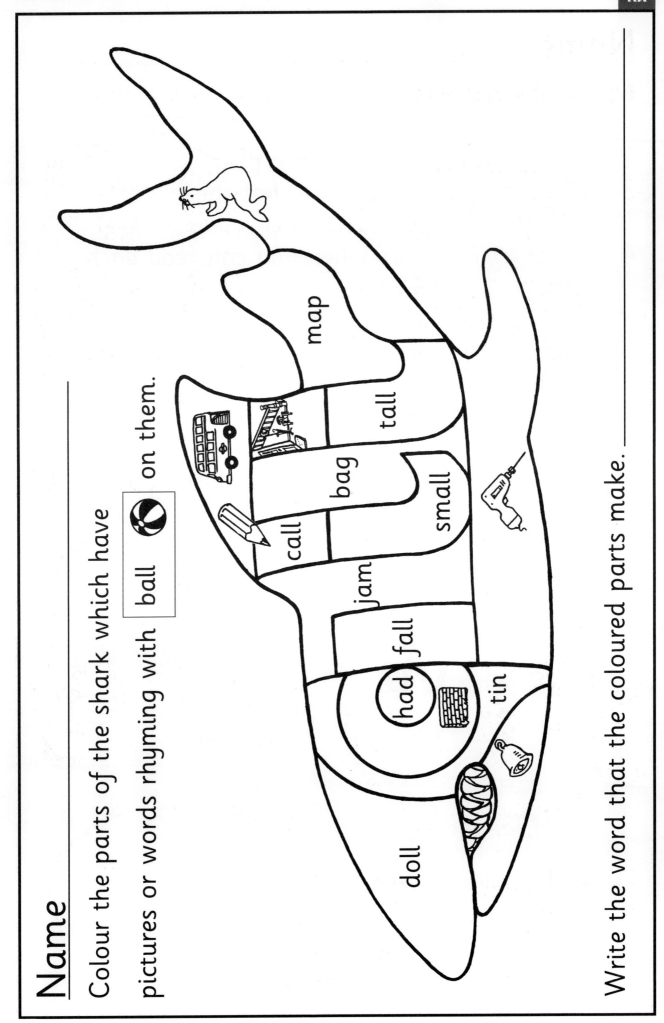 on them.

Write the word that the coloured parts make.

Name

Colour the pictures which rhyme in each rockpool.

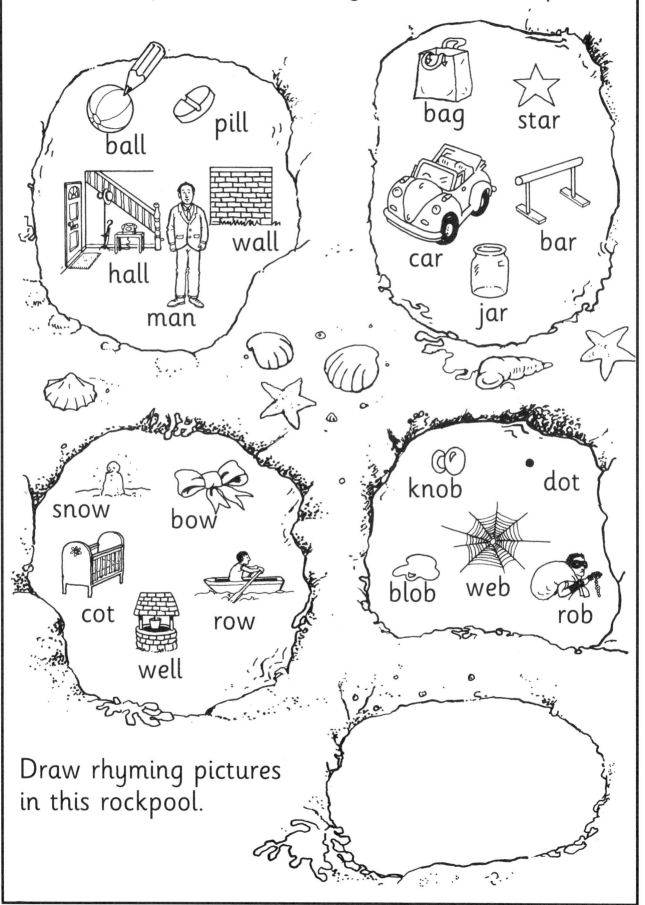

ball

pill

wall

hall

man

bag

star

car

bar

jar

snow

bow

cot

row

well

knob

dot

blob

web

rob

Draw rhyming pictures
in this rockpool.

Name

Put a ring round all the words which rhyme with

snow .

e	(s	n	o	w)	k
t	i	c	r	o	w
s	h	o	w	g	a
w	b	l	o	w	d
t	h	r	o	w	x
l	b	g	r	o	w

✂ -

grow	blow	throw 

show 	crow 

Name

Colour the starfish which rhyme with wall orange.

Colour the starfish which rhyme with knob green.

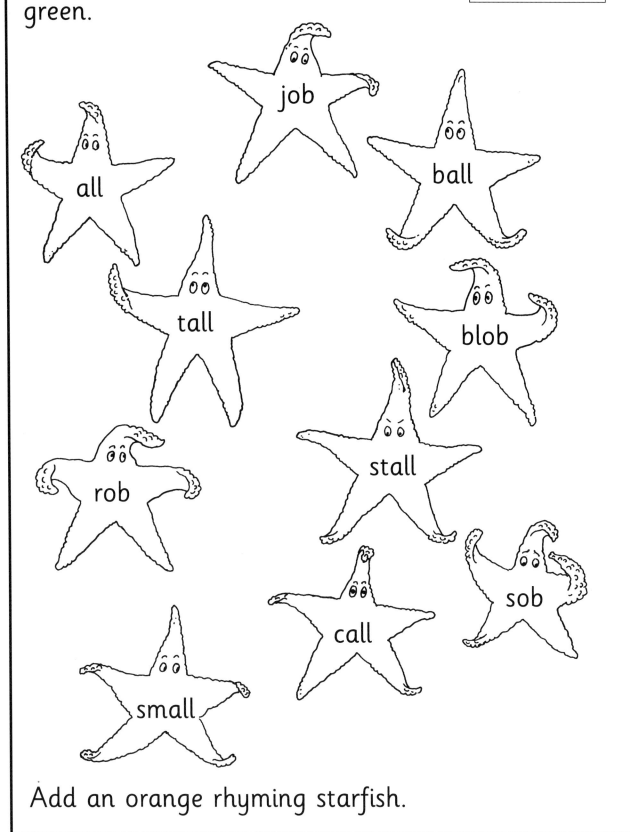

Add an orange rhyming starfish.

Name

Join up the pictures which rhyme with | star ☆ | in red.

Join up the pictures which rhyme with | ball  | in yellow.

c _____

h all _____

w _____

j _____

b _____

f _____

Finish the word by each picture.

Name _____

Finish the rhyming sentences.

Elvis played a big guitar
and became a big rock _____ .

His fans would scream and _____
and limpets hearts would throb.

Big and small, room for all.
Come you shellfish short and _____ !

| tall | star | sob |

Name

Make new rhymes.
Change the beginning of the word.
Write the new word and draw the picture.

| st | a r | ☆ | ➜ | bar |
| b | | | | |

| sn | o w | | ➜ | |
| b | | | | |

| r | o b | | ➜ | |
| kn | | | | |

| b | all | | ➜ | |
| w | | | | |

| j | a r | | ➜ | |
| c | | | | |

L

Name

Colour the things in the picture which rhyme with | cock | .

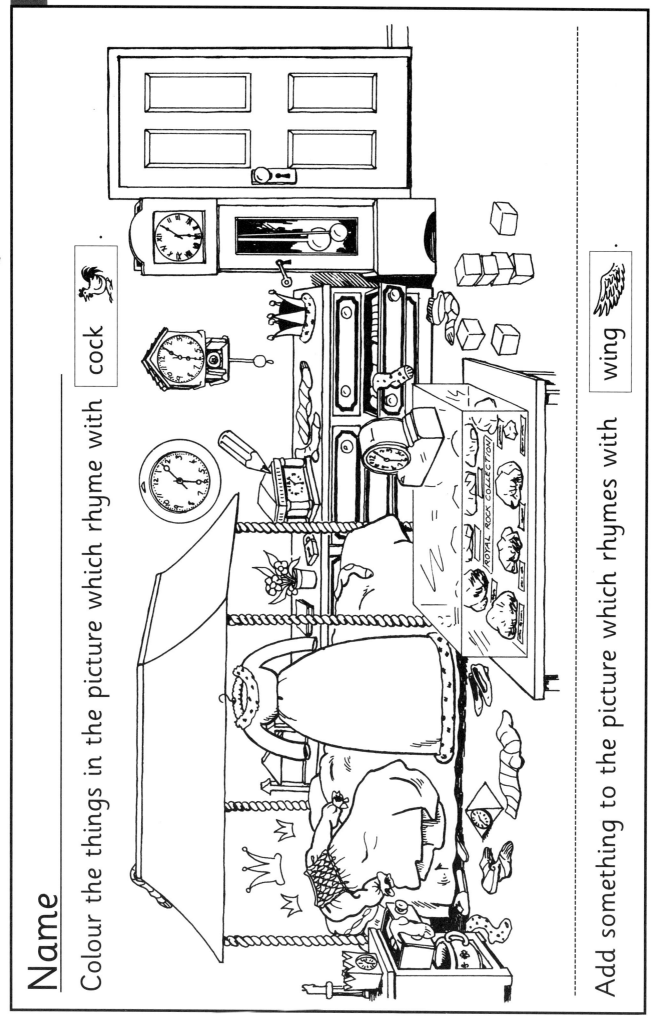

Add something to the picture which rhymes with | wing | .

Name

Join up the rhymes.

clock

plug

Name

Make the king find the clock.
Draw a line from the king to the clock.
You can only go through pictures and words which

rhyme with | king 👑 | .

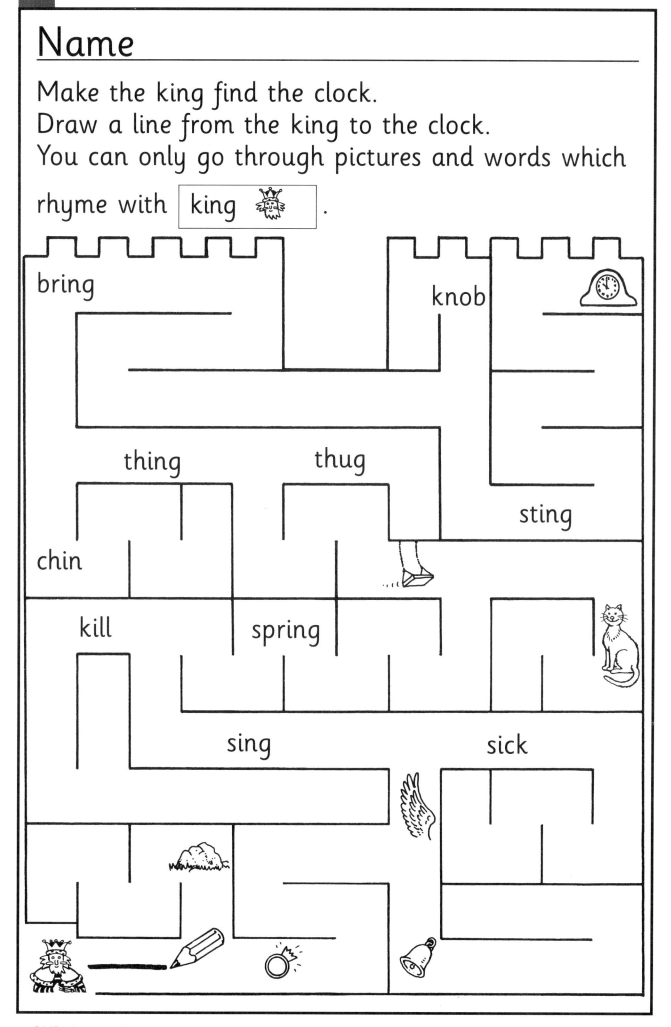

bring

knob

thing   thug

chin   sting

kill   spring

sing   sick

Name

Colour the jewels which rhyme with **plug** blue.

Colour the jewels which rhyme with **flash** red.

Colour the jewels which rhyme with **king** green.

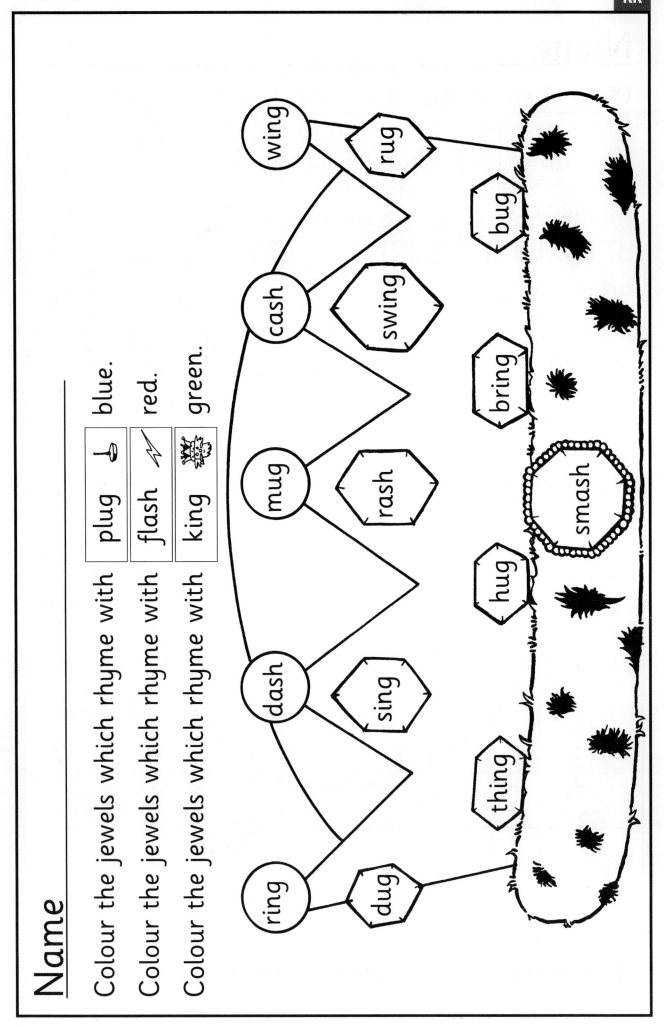

Name

Write these letters on the jug to make rhymes.

| j | b | h | m | pl | r |

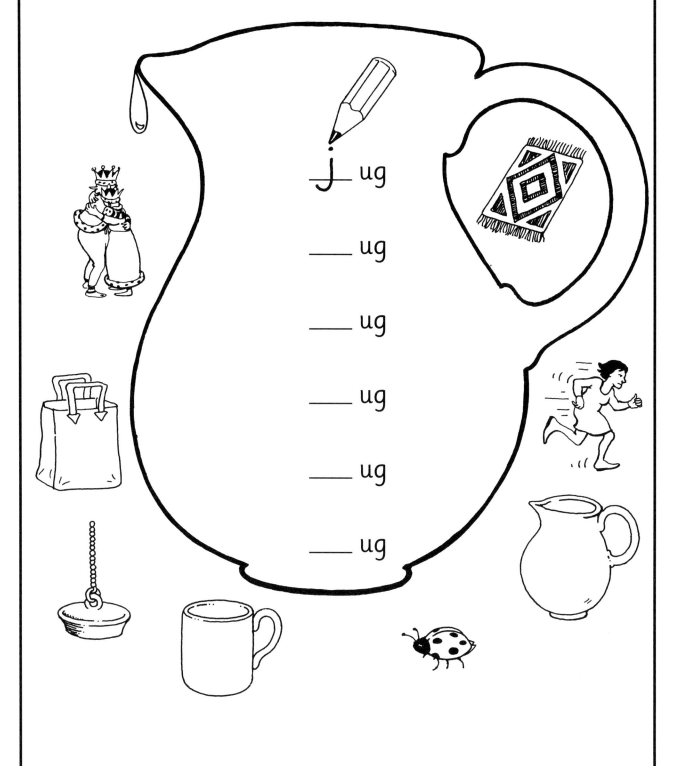

j ug

___ ug

___ ug

___ ug

___ ug

___ ug

Draw lines from the words to the pictures.

Name _____

Use the end of 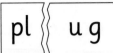 pl u g or the end of
cl o c k to finish these rhymes.

r ug

l

m

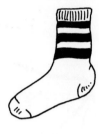
s

j

r

Write the rhyming words on the pictures.

mug
___
___
___

clock
___
___
___

Name _____

What is the king saying?
Finish the rhyming sentences.

I've got a new crown,
and I've got a gold _____ .
I've plenty of silver
and that sort of thing.

I want socks that are snug –
so my feet are as warm
as a bug in a _____ !

Oh these terrible clocks –
I'll hit them with hammers,
I'll smack them with _____ .

I'll smash them, I'll bash them,
I'll boil them and _____ them.

| rocks | mash | rug | ring |

Name

Colour the socks which rhyme in each drawer.

dug   leg   bug

splash   clash   small

dock   truck   rock

drill   wing   thing

Add a rhyming sock to each drawer.

Name

All the words on the sock rhyme with sock.
The letters are in the wrong order.
Write the letters in the right order.

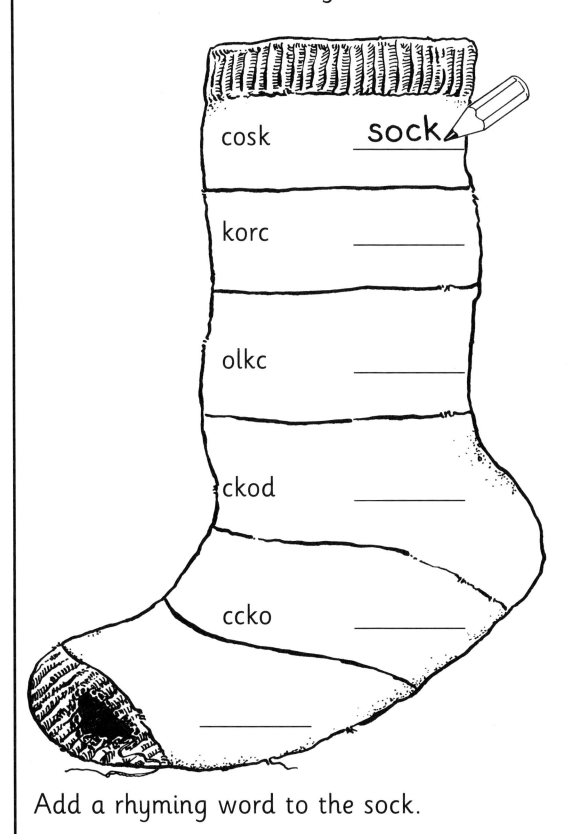

cosk   <u>sock</u>

korc   _____

olkc   _____

ckod   _____

ccko   _____

_____

Add a rhyming word to the sock.

   87

Name

Join up the rhymes.

sack

hush

mess

long

back

Name

Colour the pictures which rhyme in each cheese.

brush

hush

shell

nut

rush

king

gong

long

song

shop

sack

duck

back

black

track

dress

chess

mess

bell

chip

Put a ring round the cheese with the
most rhymes in it.

Name

Put a ring round the four words which rhyme with

long .

e	h	l	o	n	g
i	w	r	o	n	g
k	l	g	n	y	t
g	o	n	g	d	i
b	w	s	o	n	g
s	t	r	o	n	g

song   gong

strong   wrong 1+1≠3

Name

Write these letters on the rack to make rhymes.

| r | b | cr | qu | s | sn |

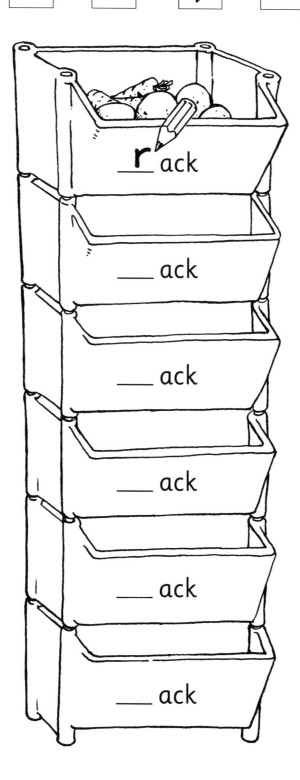

___r ack

___ ack

___ ack

___ ack

___ ack

___ ack

Draw a picture to match each word.

Name

Colour the dresses which rhyme on each line.

dress press mess fell chess

sack shock track back pack

long song king wrong strong

brush hush rush crush dash

Add these dresses to the right lines.

black blush gong less

Name

Use the end of [s | a c k] or the end of

[br | u s h] 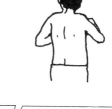 to finish these rhymes.

[sn | ack]

[b |]

[h |]

[bl |]

[tr |]

[r |]

Write the rhyming words on the pictures.

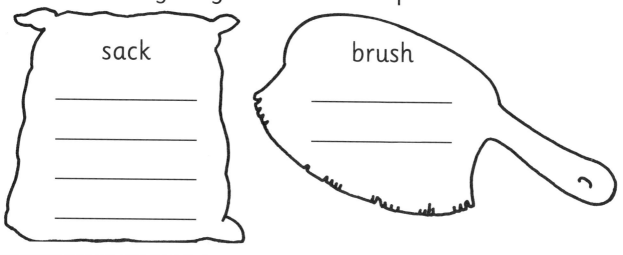

sack

brush

Name

Can you guess who has a dress? Join up the dots.

Write what Gran has given each
person in the boxes.

Name

Finish the rhyming sentences.

You must have gone out in a rush.
We don't need a new toilet _____ .

I wanted some tacks,
not some black plastic _____ .

You didn't go shopping for long.
And whose is this shiny brass _____ ?

Some mustard and cress,
I couldn't buy _____ .

| less | gong | brush | sacks |

Name

Make new rhymes.
Change the beginning of the word.
Write the new word and draw the picture.

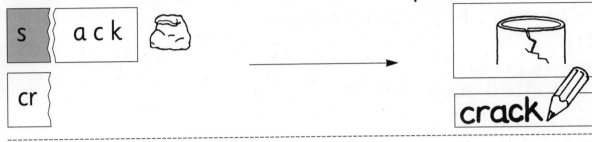

s | a c k

cr |

crack

m | e s s

dr |

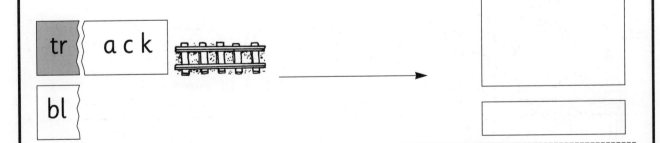

h | u s h

br |

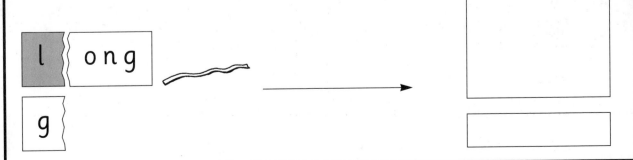

tr | a c k

bl |

l | o n g

g |

Name

Find the dragon which rhymes.

kick

moss

rang

stick

hut

Name

Draw a line from the robbers to the town.
You can only go through pictures and words which

rhyme with chick .

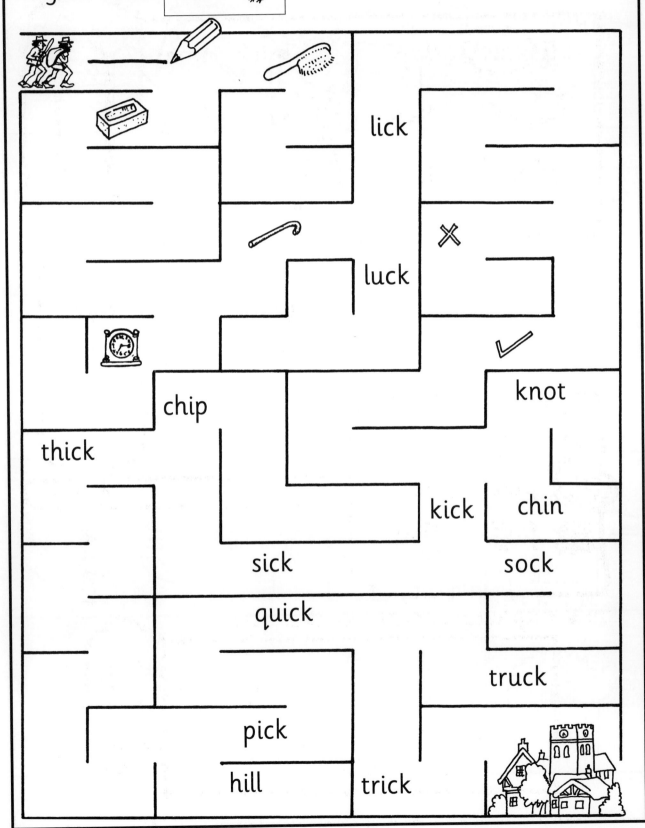

lick

luck

knot

chip

thick

kick   chin

sick   sock

quick

truck

pick

hill   trick

Name

The pictures in each tool rhyme.
Put rings round the right words.

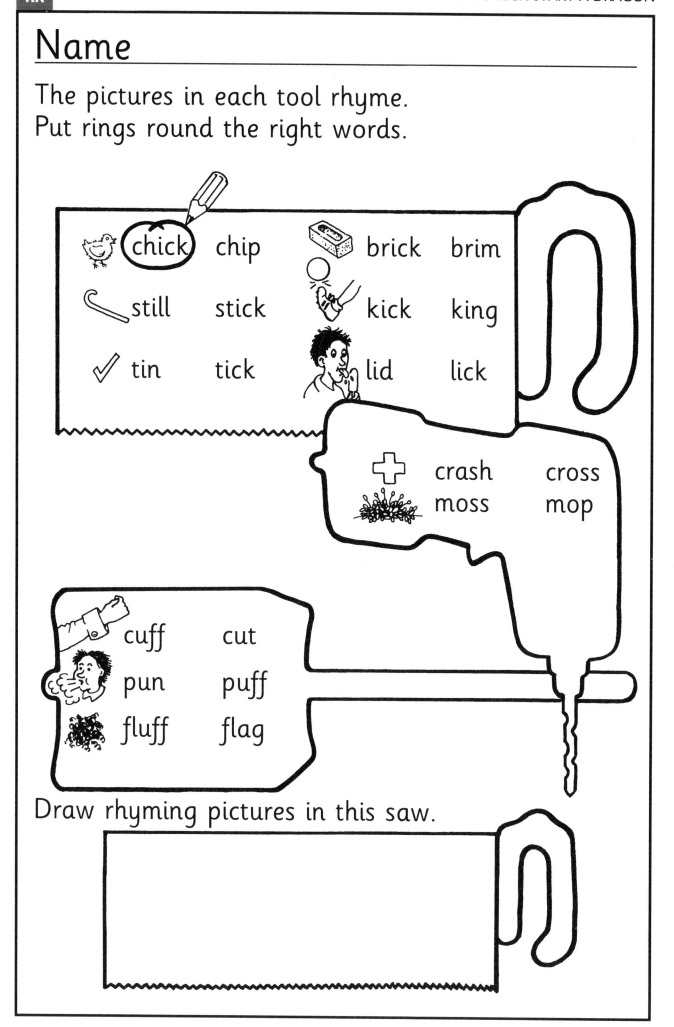

(chick) chip   brick   brim

still   stick   kick   king

tin   tick   lid   lick

crash   cross
moss   mop

cuff   cut
pun   puff
fluff   flag

Draw rhyming pictures in this saw.

RR

Name

Colour the robbers which rhyme with **chick** 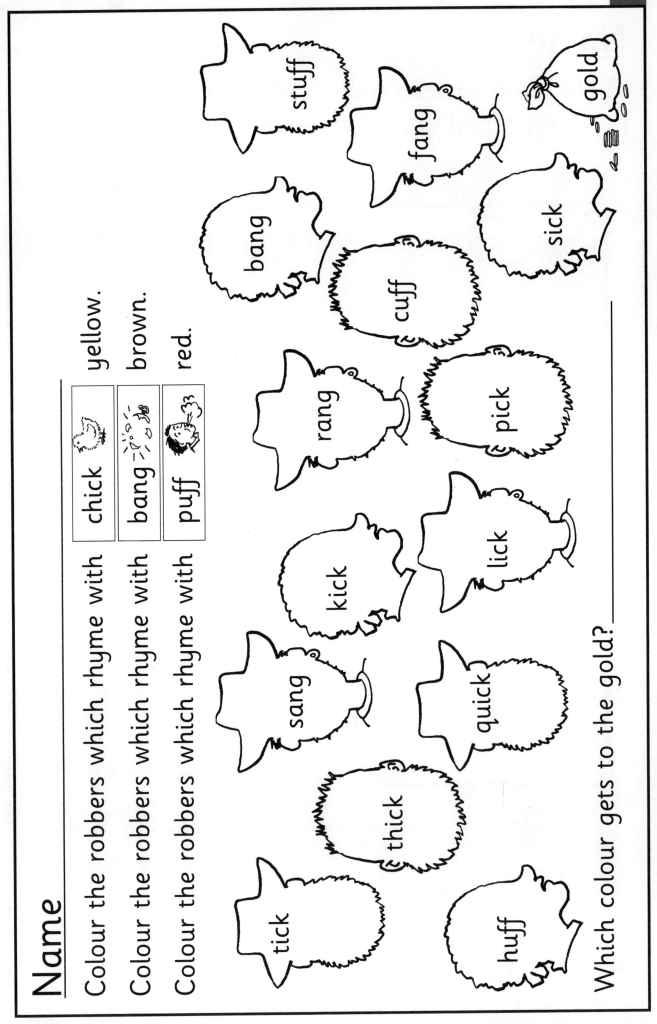 yellow.

Colour the robbers which rhyme with **bang** brown.

Colour the robbers which rhyme with **puff** red.

stuff

fang

gold?

bang

cuff

sick

rang

pick

kick

lick

sang

quick

thick

tick

huff

Which colour gets to the gold? _____

Name

Write these letters on the chick to make rhymes.

ch	br	k	l	st	t

chick

___ ick

___ ick

___ ick

___ ick

___ ick

Draw lines from the words to the pictures.

Name _____

Finish the rhyming sentences.

This dragon must roar,
and huff and _____ .

The Mayor called a meeting,
she looked quite sick.
She stood on the steps,
and she tapped her _____ .

Then up spoke Nick,
and up spoke Ross.
'We've got an idea,
if you won't be _____ .'

All sorts of springs
and sprockets sprang.
Then all of a sudden
it went off _____ !

| bang | cross | puff | stick |

Name

Make new rhymes.
Change the beginning of the word.
Write the new word and draw the picture.

m } o s s

cr }

cr

p } u f f

c }

st } i c k

br }

s } a n g

b }

Name

These children are thinking about rhymes.
Add a rhyme to each one.

Draw a picture of yourself thinking about rhymes.

Name

Look at the picture clues.
Write the rhymes in the crosswords.

L

Name

Draw something which rhymes in each animal's home.

I spy with my little eye something which rhymes with
cat.

I spy with my little eye something which rhymes with
dog.

I spy with my little eye something which rhymes with
hen.

I spy with my little eye something which rhymes with
chick.

Name

Put a ring round all the words which rhyme with

stung 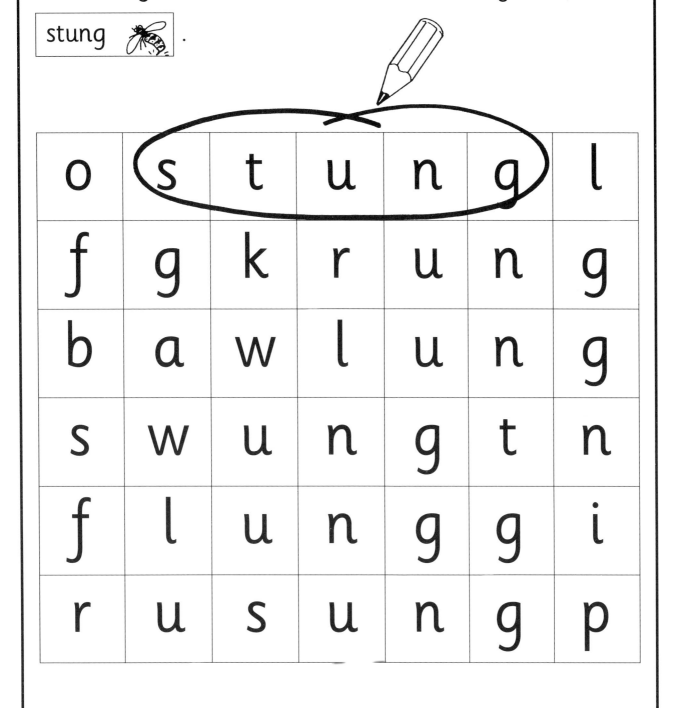 .

o	s	t	u	n	g	l
f	g	k	r	u	n	g
b	a	w	l	u	n	g
s	w	u	n	g	t	n
f	l	u	n	g	g	i
r	u	s	u	n	g	p

flung	rung	sung

| swung | lung | |

Name

Whose homes are these?

'This is my home,' said _____ .

'This is my home,' said _____ .

Draw your home.

Name

Write these letters on the snakes to make words which match the pictures.

| sn | cr | dr | gr | h | st |

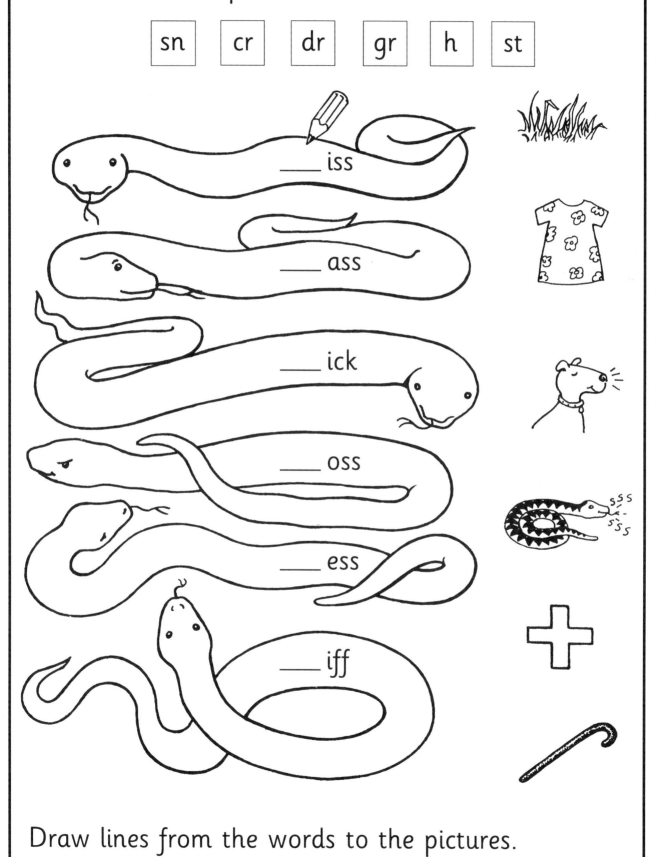

___ iss

___ ass

___ ick

___ oss

___ ess

___ iff

Draw lines from the words to the pictures.

Name

Finish the rhyming sentences.
Draw each animal in its home.

'This is my home,' said Snake,
with a soft hiss.

'This is what I would _____.'

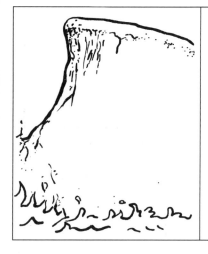

'This is my home,' said Gull,
with a high cry.

'On this _____
where the stiff winds
lift me sky high.'

'This is my home,' said Bear,
with a sure snore.

'I let winter pass –
when ice is like _____.'

| glass | miss | cliff |

Name

Make new rhymes.
Change the beginning of the word.
Write the new word and draw the picture.

| sn | iff |
| cl | |

| h | iss |
| k | |

| r | ung |
| st | |

| gl | ass |
| gr | |

Name

Colour the seals which rhyme in each pool.

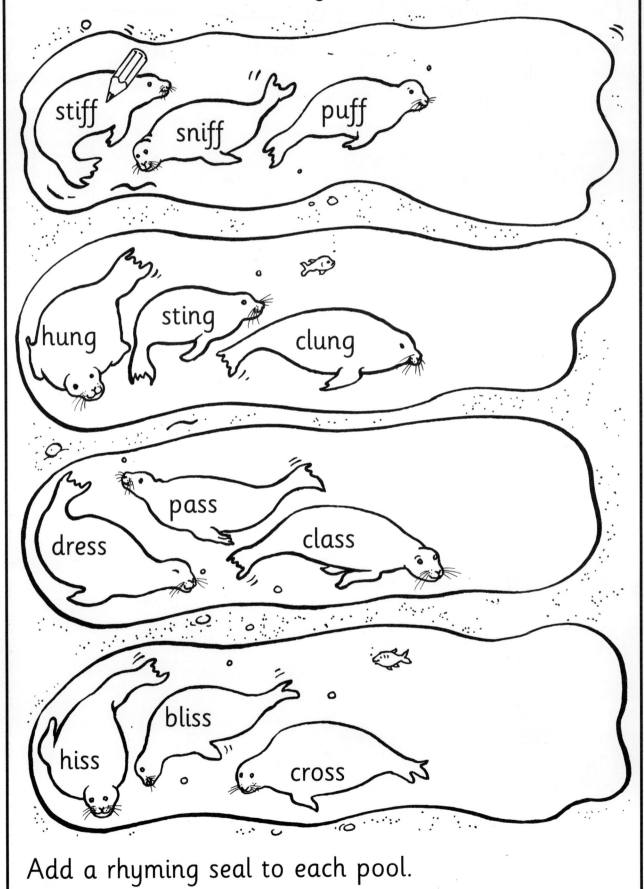

Add a rhyming seal to each pool.

Name

Look at the picture clues.
Write the rhymes in the crosswords.

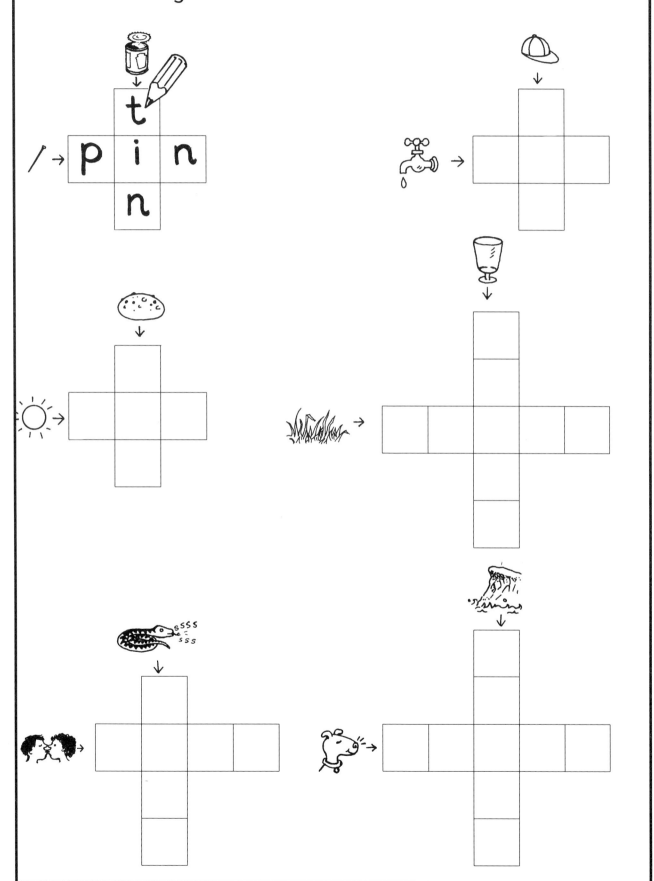

Name

All the words in the glass rhyme with

grass 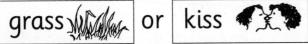 or kiss .

The letters are in the wrong order.
Write the letters in the right order.

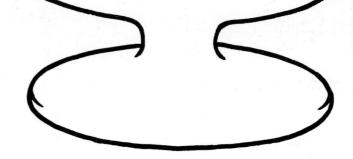

glass

lasgs   _____

sish   _____

smis   _____

sspa   _____

scsla   _____

bslsi   _____

Name

Play I spy
Read the words on the picture frame.
Look for something which rhymes with each word in the picture.
Colour the word and the thing the same colour.

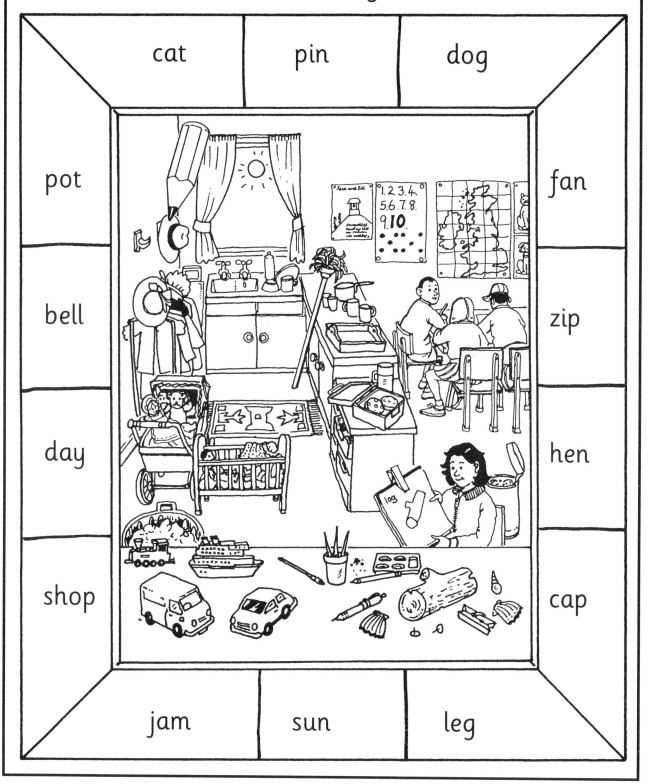

| cat | pin | dog |

pot   fan

bell   zip

day   hen

shop   cap

| jam | sun | leg |

Name _____

Play I spy
Read the words on the picture frame.
Look for something which rhymes with
each word in the picture.
Colour the word and the thing the same colour.

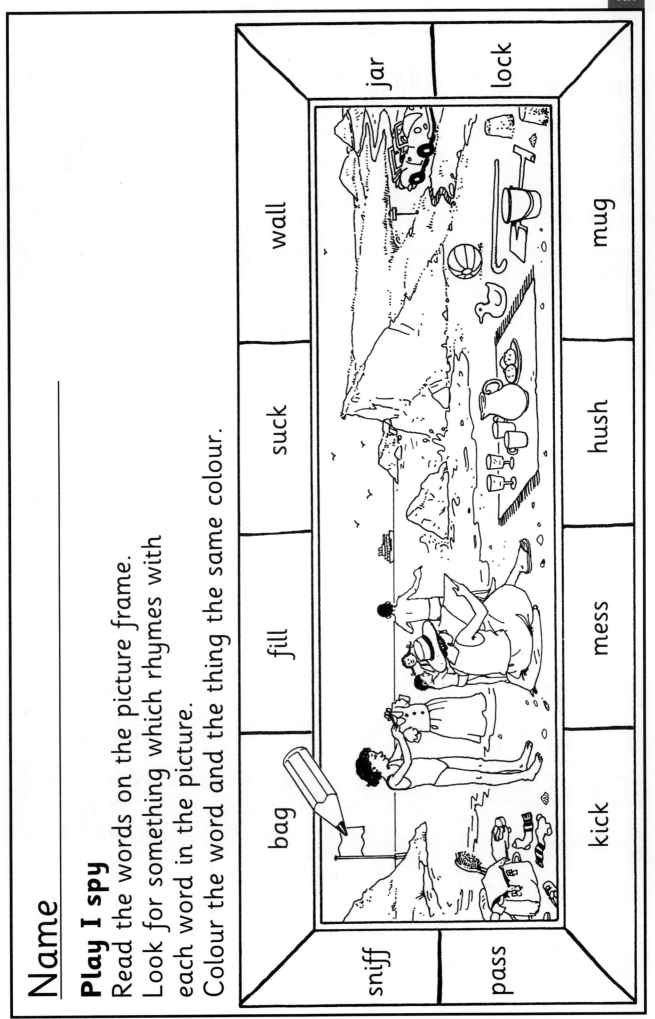

jar

lock

wall

suck

fill

bag

sniff

pass

mug

hush

mess

kick

Name

Trap the Mungle Flap game

Start

Finish

Throw a dice to move.

Then say a word which rhymes with the picture you land on.

Miss a go if you can't say a word.

Name

Join up the ball which rhymes with each bat.

Name

Put the lids on the pens by reading the words.

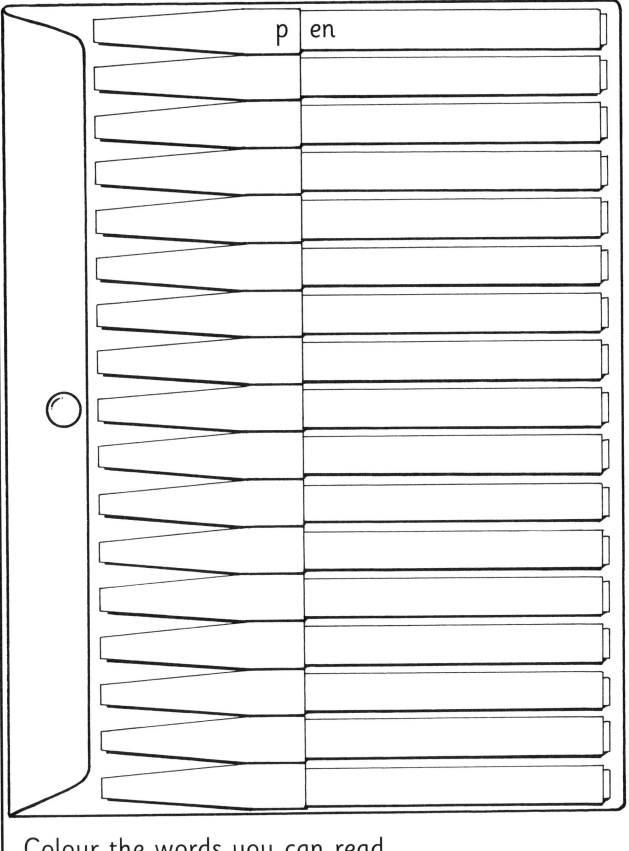

p | en

Colour the words you can read.

Name _____

Put a ring round all the words which rhyme

with _____ .

Name

Climb up the ladder.
Draw something which rhymes in each space.

Write the rhymes on the rungs of the ladder.

Name

Draw a family of things which rhyme on each scarf.

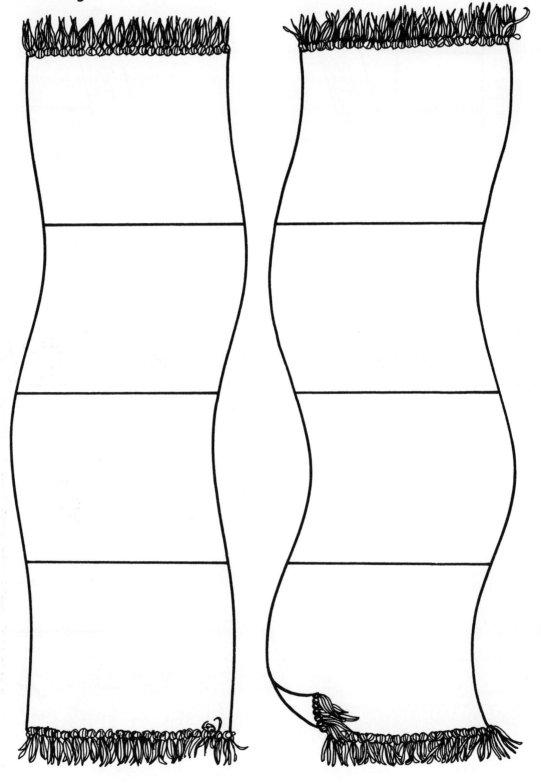

Write the rhymes below each picture.

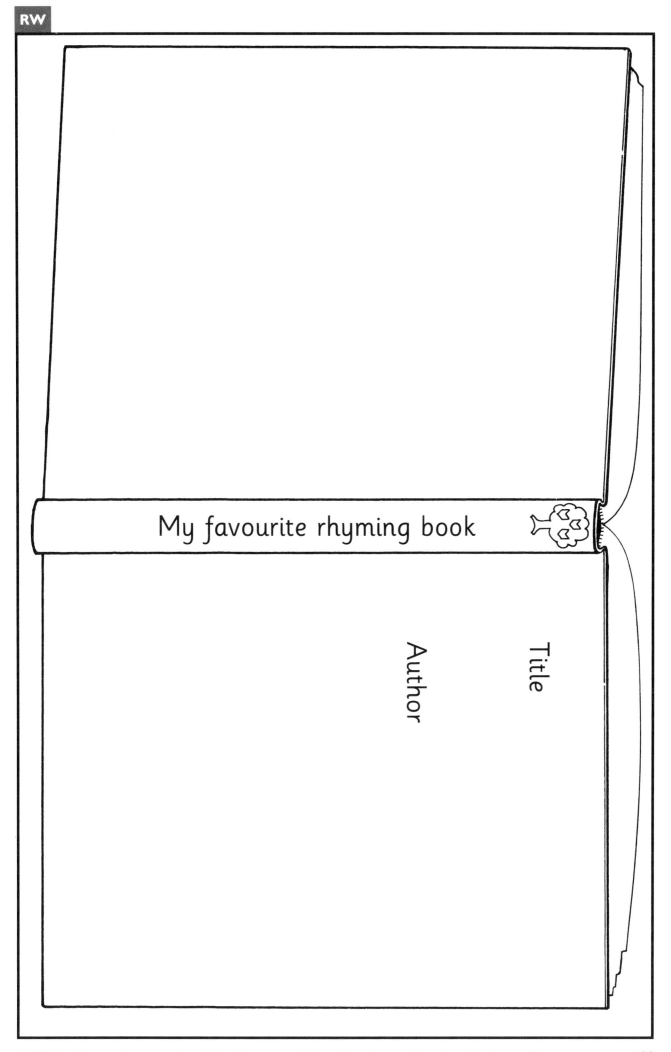

My favourite rhyming book

Title

Author

Name _____

What happened in the story?
Tell the story again in the boxes.

1	2	3
4	5	6

RW